Queens, Queens, Queens

Queens,

Queens,

Queens

SELECTED AND EDITED BY
HELEN O'CLERY

FRANKLIN WATTS, INC.   575 LEXINGTON AVE.
NEW YORK   *watts*   N. Y. 10022
international

ACKNOWLEDGMENTS

The selections in this book are used by permission and special arrangements with the proprietors of their respective copyrights who are listed below. The editor's and publisher's thanks to all who made this collection possible.

The editor and publisher have made every effort to trace ownership of all material contained herein. It is their belief that the necessary permission from publishers, authors, and authorized agents have been obtained in all cases. In the event of any questions arising as to the use of any material, the editor and publisher express regret for any error unconsciously made and will be pleased to make the necessary correction in future editions of the book.

A. & C. Black Ltd. for "Mary Queen of Scots," by Elizabeth Grierson. This selection is from the book SCOTTISH KEEPS AND CASTLES, by Elizabeth Grierson. Reprinted by permission.

Basil Blackwell for "Queen Esther, Who Saved Her People," by Eleanor Farjeon. This selection is from the book MIGHTY MEN, by Eleanor Farjeon. Reprinted by permission.

Doubleday & Company, Inc. for "Eleanor of Aquitaine," by Nora Lofts. This selection is from the book ELEANOR THE QUEEN, by Nora Lofts, copyright © 1955 by Nora Lofts. Reprinted by permission. For "Juliana of the Netherlands," by Alden Hatch. This selection is from the book BERNHARD, PRINCE OF THE NETHERLANDS, by Alden Hatch. First American edition, 1962 © 1962 by H. J. W. Becht's Uitgeversmaatschappij N. V., Amsterdam. English text © 1962 by George G. Harrap & Company, Ltd. Reprinted by permission of Doubleday & Company, Inc.

Dodd, Mead & Company and W. H. Allen & Co., London, for "A Traveling Queen," by Helen Cathcart. This selection is from the book HER MAJESTY THE QUEEN: THE STORY OF ELIZABETH II, by Helen Cathcart, copyright © 1962 by Helen Cathcart. Reprinted by permission.

Duell, Sloan and Pearce for "Elizabeth I of England," by Elswyth Thane. This selection is from the book THE TUDOR WENCH, by Elswyth Thane, copyright 1932, 1960 by Elswyth Thane Beebe. Reprinted by permission.

J. B. Lippincott Company for "Hail, Queen Elizabeth," by Eleanor Farjeon. This selection is from the book KINGS AND QUEENS, by Eleanor Farjeon and Herbert Farjeon, copyright 1932 by Eleanor and Herbert Farjeon. Reprinted by permission.

Julian Messner, Inc. for "Cleopatra," by Iris Noble. This selection is from the book EGYPT'S QUEEN, CLEOPATRA, by Iris Noble, copyright © 1963 by Iris Noble. Reprinted by permission. For "Carlota, American Empress," by Nancy Barnes. This selection is from the book CARLOTA, AMERICAN EMPRESS, by Nancy Barnes, copyright 1943 by Nancy Barnes. Reprinted by permission of Julian Messner, Division of Pocket Books, Inc.

Contents

Contents

About This Book

I SUPPOSE the most fascinating game any of us has ever played is that of "Kings and Queens." I remember when I was very small, we played this game. My elder brother was the king and an older cousin was the queen. A younger girl cousin and I were amongst their slaves. The king and queen ordered us to climb into our grandmother's garden, pick pocketfuls of plums and bring them to their Royal Highnesses. When we had successfully done this, their Majesties ate the plums and threw us the stones. No doubt they had a lot of fun. As a matter of fact, we also enjoyed ourselves, as we knew that "they" would be sent away to boarding school the following year, and that one of us would be queen over the younger brothers, sisters, and cousins. Just then, the decision as to which of us would be queen did not arise, so we could sing the Gilbert and Sullivan song, which begins "Then one of us will be a Queen."

Looking back upon the scene, I am surprised that their Majesties did not chastise us for gloating so openly over their imminent overthrow—but perhaps they were already feeling the effects of a surfeit of plums.

Seriously, however, queens are fascinating to study. It is seldom in history that a "regular Royal Queen" got the opportunity to rule. Queen Consorts there were in plenty, and many of them ruled from behind the throne. But even the very ancient peoples who worshiped the Mother Goddess were not partial to queens, and only glorified them long after they were dead. Of the prehistoric races, only the Amazons were real feminists, and they had to kill all their menfolk before they could take the power into their own hands.

Cleopatra did much the same thing when her time came, though she mainly confined the killing to her brothers, who were the only people likely to come between her and the throne. After clearing the way in this manner, however, she showed no further Amazonian characteristics, but quite blatantly used her feminine charms to enroll first Caesar and then Mark Antony upon her side. If she had managed to leave it at that, she might have been the greatest monarch of all time, but fortunately, or unfortunately—according to how you look at it—she inadvertently lost her heart to Antony. Thus she comes down in history as a wonderfully romantic woman rather than a capable queen.

The list of famous queens is a long one. There would not be room for stories about them all in one book. Their names are like a song: Theodora and Isabella, Boadicea and Sigrid, Marie Antoinette, Bloody Mary and Maria Theresa, and Tzu Hsi. Many were beautiful; some were cruel. It is not easy to be a queen and some of the beautiful and brave were also unhappy. Even knowing all this, how many of us can resist playing the game, "If I were Queen?"

Although kings are still in the majority, it is interesting to find that at the present time more queens reign in their own right than during any other period of history.

Helen O'Clery

Ireland, 1965

A REGULAR ROYAL QUEEN

by W. S. GILBERT

Then one of us will be a Queen,
  And sit on a golden throne,
    With a crown instead
    Of a hat on her head,
  And diamonds all her own!
With a beautiful robe of gold and green,
  I've always understood;
    I wonder whether
    She'd wear a feather?
  I rather think she should.

And noble lords will scrape and bow,
  And double themselves in two,
    And open their eyes
    In bland surprise,
  At whatever she likes to do.
And everybody will roundly vow
  She's fair as flowers in May,
    And say, "How clever!"
    At whatsoever
  She condescends to say.

She'll drive about in a carriage and pair,
  With the King on her left-hand side.
    And a milk-white horse
    As a matter of course,
  Whenever she wants to ride.
With beautiful silken shoes to wear
Upon her dainty feet,
    And endless stocks
    Of beautiful frocks,
  And as much as she likes to eat!

1

Oh, 'tis a glorious thing I ween,
To be a regular Royal Queen!
No half-and-half affair, I mean,
No half-and-half affair,
But a right-down regular, regular,
Regular, regular, Royal Queen!

HELEN HOKE

Isis, first Queen of Egypt

Isis was the first queen of Egypt, and perhaps the first queen in all the world. She lived over five thousand years ago. When history began, her story had already become a legend, and in the first records she was honored as a goddess.

WHEN THE HISTORY of Egypt was just beginning, there lived a wise young woman named Isis. She was skilled in many arts, and her knowledge of magic was as great as that of the gods. But this was not enough to satisfy her.

"Why shouldn't I be mistress of all the earth?" she asked herself one day as she bathed in the river Nile. "If I but knew the secret name of Ra, the Sun-god, I would know how to go about

From TALES OF ANCIENT EGYPT, by Helen Hoke.

3

this." She stepped out of the river and sat upon the bank, staring into the water and thinking.

Ra was the greatest of the Egyptian gods. Among men he had many names, but the secret name was known to no one. Not even the other gods. And it was this secret name that gave Ra his special power.

A fire of curiosity began to consume Isis. She *had* to know this secret name. She searched through all her wisdom—and at last hit upon a scheme.

The Sun-god came from the world of darkness every morning, and journeyed across the sky. Isis watched him carefully, and on one very warm day, she noticed that drops of water fell to the earth from the Sun-god's forehead. Quickly gathering up the drops and the earth upon which they had fallen, Isis shaped a tiny serpent and breathed life into it. Then she uttered a magic spell over it, and the next day, when Ra passed that way, she threw the serpent in his path.

The moment the Sun-god stepped on the creature it bit him —and because it was a magic serpent, and frightened as well, its poison had extraordinary power. Ra cried aloud as the poison raced through his body. Being a god, he had never felt pain before and now he did not know what to do. He fell on the shore of the Nile and writhed in agony.

Suddenly Isis appeared before him. "My lord," she said, "you are in great trouble."

"Indeed I am," replied the Sun-god. "I, who am immortal, have never known a thing like this."

"Ah," said Isis craftily, "I, being mortal, have. What you are feeling is *pain*."

"Since you know what this is, do you know how to stop it?"

"Yes," said Isis.

"Well, then!" Ra cried. "Stop it!"

"Not so fast," Isis told him coolly. "I can stop human pain, but you, yourself, have said you are a god. Therefore I need something greater than my simple mortal charms to aid you. I need your secret name!"

"*What!*" shouted Ra. "No one in the world must know my secret name but I!"

"And I," said Isis stubbornly. "Else I cannot cure the pain."

"I cannot bear it!" groaned the Sun-god.

The woman only looked at him and made no move to aid him.

The Sun-god's anger, added to the serpent's poison, nearly set Ra on fire. "You are but a woman!" cried the Sun-god. "If I tell you my secret name it will make you immortal, too!"

"I shall try to bear with that," Isis said.

"Very well. Lean close and I will whisper that which no one else but I has known until this moment."

Isis put her ear to his lips and as the secret name passed between them, her eyes glowed with triumph. She then put her lips to the wound upon the Sun-god and drew out the poison, and with it drew immortality for herself. In that moment Isis became a goddess.

But, although she was now a goddess, Isis continued to live as a mortal woman among the people of the earth. In due time, when the good King Osiris was seeking a wife, he chose to wed her, for she was not only beautiful, but also wise.

They ruled Egypt together for many years. Osiris made farming implements and taught men how to till the rich soil near the Nile, and how to sow grain and how to reap it. He made his people live in peace, and he invented the art of picture writing, so that Egyptian history could at last be set down.

Isis became as a mother to the Egyptian nation. She taught the women some of her healing arts. She also taught them to weave cloth and to sew it together, and to make pottery out of the clay found near the river Nile. She loved all the children of Egypt, even as she loved her little son Horus—but she never breathed to anyone her own secret of immortality. Not even Osiris knew that he had married a goddess.

Under their rule Egypt prospered and all men loved them. All, that is, but a few who were under the influence of the jealous brother of Osiris, Set. Being a goddess, Isis could see the wickedness in Set's heart and she warned her husband against him. But Osiris could not believe that there was evil in his own brother.

One day, Set invited Osiris to his palace on the river Nile. That night there was a huge banquet for the King. There was much feasting and drinking and merrymaking.

Suddenly eight huge Ethiopian slaves marched into the great hall, bearing upon their shoulders a large chest. This they set upon the floor and Set said:

"My brother! See this magnificent chest. It is made of the most precious wood I could find. It is bound with gold and silver bands and, as you see, I have had gems set into the lid. I shall give this chest to one of my guests—and you, dear brother, shall help me decide which one it shall be."

"How can I do that?" Osiris asked.

"Well," said the evil brother. "It will really be simple. The chest shall belong to that one of my guests who best fits into it. He must, however, fit into it exactly. Therefore he must not be too tall or too short, too fat or too thin. And, you, my brother, shall be the judge of all, as befits your rank."

"An unusual game," Osiris commented smiling. "Proceed."

Now the guests at this banquet had been carefully selected for two reasons: one, because they hated the good Osiris and wished to make the evil Set Pharaoh in his place; two, because not one of them could comfortably fit into the chest.

After all had tried and this became evident, Osiris said, "Now what do you suggest, dear brother?"

Set had the answer ready. "Since obviously I am too short for the chest, you are the only one left to try it—but first, let me hold your crown."

"Of course," replied the unsuspecting Osiris, and handing the crown over to his brother, he stepped into the chest and lay down full length, "Why," he exclaimed, "it is a perfect fit! As if it were made for me!"

"And so it was!" shouted the traitor Set, and with a mighty heave he slammed the lid shut upon Osiris.

The Ethiopian slaves were then ordered to lock the clasps and take the chest up on their shoulders. Thus they marched out of the palace, straight to a deep part of the river, and heaved the chest into the rushing water.

So the good Osiris perished, and the chest bearing his body floated down the river Nile. Seeing it pass, the birds ceased their singing, the fish sank to the bottom of the river, and the wind, like a great sigh of sorrow, swept over the land.

Isis, playing in the royal palace with her little son Horus, lifted up her face and listened to the wind. With a brokenhearted cry she buried her face in her hands. "Set has slain Osiris!" she wailed. "My beloved husband is dead!"

She had lived as a mortal woman for so long that in her sorrow she did not immediately remember that she was a goddess who knew the secret of life and death. All at once, however, power and knowledge came to her and she leaped to her feet. If she could but find the body of Osiris she might yet bring him back to life! But first she must put her little son Horus into a safe place.

Taking the child, she hastened to a distant part of the kingdom and gave him into the care of a dear friend. Then she cast a spell over the area, so none could find the boy and harm him. Having done this, Isis set out on her sad search along the river Nile.

Many people had seen the mysterious chest float down the river, but none knew where it had gone. At long last some children told Isis that they had found the chest, cast up by the waves into a bush near the shore.

"And then," the children cried, "the bush grew into a great tree, all around the chest!"

"Yes, yes!" Isis cried. "Where is this tree? Show it to me!"

"We can't," said a little boy. "The tree was so tall and so straight, our king had it made into a pillar for his palace."

Within that pillar was the body of her beloved husband, Isis knew, and hastened to the palace. But she did not go inside. Instead she sat weeping beside the fountain. Presently the Queen's maidens came out and seeing the sad stranger spoke kindly to her.

Isis smiled at the maidens. "You are so kind to me, a lonely wanderer," she said, "that I wish to do something for you. I am skilled in beauty arts. Let me braid your hair more becomingly." And this she did, and as she arranged the maidens' hair, each one seemed to become more beautiful. As Isis worked with the raven tresses of the girls, she breathed upon their hair and it instantly took on a wonderful fragrance.

When the maidens returned to the palace they ran to their queen, Astarte, and told her of the stranger at the fountain.

"Remarkable," said the Queen. "And the scent which she has given you is exquisite. Bring this woman to me."

And so Isis came into the palace, looking like a humble servant, for all that she was a far greater queen than Astarte. But though she served the Queen well, she spent every moment possible playing with one of the young princes, who was rather sickly. Whenever Isis was with the child, Astarte noticed that the little prince appeared stronger and rosier, and whenever she left him, he pined for her. Before long, Isis was made chief nurse for the child and the prince thrived under her care.

There were some in the palace who were jealous of the preference shown to the stranger, and they spied upon her. One night, after Isis had put the little prince to bed, these jealous ones peeked through a crack in the door and what they saw sent them racing to Astarte. They related so horrifying a tale, that the mother forgot all her queenly dignity. Picking up her fine linen skirts she ran down the palace halls and burst into the room where Isis had the young prince.

Imagine the mother's feelings when she saw her child lying in a pile of burning sticks and a swallow flying around the flames and twittering mournfully.

With a loud cry Astarte rushed forward and plucked her child from the flames.

In that instant Isis returned to her human form—and to all her queenly dignity. "You have deprived the prince of immortality!" she said. "Another few moments and all would have been accomplished." Then she told the frightened mother who she was, and Astarte fell on her knees and begged forgiveness.

"I forgive you," Isis said sadly. "But you must give me the central pillar from this palace, for it contains the body of my slain husband, Osiris."

"You shall have it," Astarte promised, and commanded slaves to take the pillar down at once. "Why did you not tell me your story in the beginning?" she then asked gently.

Isis shook her head. "After the treacherous murder of my husband, I dared trust no one," she said.

When the slaves had taken the pillar down, Isis caused it to be split open, and there was the casket. A magic boat of papyrus reeds was built for Isis, and having had the casket put in it, she guided the boat into the marshes of the Nile.

There she opened the casket and gazed at the face of her beloved. At daybreak, she spoke magic words over Osiris, calling his soul back into his body, as she breathed into his nostrils.

Again and again she did this, but, alas, the soul of Osiris had been gone too long from his body. It was of no avail.

In her grief Isis cried out in a terrible voice: "By the secret name of Ra, let the sun stand in the heavens, for Osiris is indeed dead!"

And, lo! the sun stood still, and time stood still, and everything all over the world stood still.

And then there was a mighty rushing through the air. Suddenly Thoth, the god of wisdom, stood before the grieving Isis. "What has happened here?" he asked, and Isis told him her story.

"And now," she finished, "all my power is as nothing, for I cannot bring my beloved back to life."

Thoth shook his mighty head. "It is not right that you should," he said. "He that has known the mysteries of death cannot walk among mortal men again. But because Osiris was a good man and a great king, and because your love is so strong for him, I will recall his soul into his body and make him live forever—"

Isis' eyes brightened, but Thoth held up his hand. "Osiris shall live forever as a king among the deserving spirits."

The Queen bowed her head before the wisdom of Thoth. "If I could but see my beloved husband alive once more—if only for a moment . . ." she whispered.

"Look, then," Thoth said.

And there was Osiris, standing beside Isis, smiling. He touched her face, then following the god Thoth, he vanished among the reeds and rushes of the marsh.

For a long time Isis stood on that spot. Finally she realized that for her this task was finished, but she had another. There was her little son Horus to fetch from his hiding place. She must raise him and teach him to be as fine a man as his father Osiris had been in this world.

So, with her son, Isis lived at the edge of the marshland. Here she taught the people all manner of useful skills and healed the sick. Everyone who knew her loved her. And whenever any of her people died, Isis was always there to comfort the family.

"Weep not," she said. "Your loved one has gone to live forever in the kingdom of Osiris—there, beyond the marshes, among the spirits of the good."

RUDYARD KIPLING

Balkis

This story is about Balkis, Queen of Sheba, the favorite queen in the great King Solomon's harem. Solomon reigned over Israel more than nine hundred years before Christ. The Bible tells us of his fabulous wisdom and of his fabulous wealth. But this delightful story is found neither in the Bible nor in any history book.

THIS, O MY BEST BELOVED, is a story—a new and a wonderful story—a story quite different from the other stories—a story about The Most Wise Sovereign Suleiman-bin-Daoud—Solomon the son of David.

Suleiman-bin-Daoud was wise. He understood what the beasts said, what the birds said, what the fishes said, and what the insects said. He understood everything, from the bishop on the bench to the hyssop on the wall; and Balkis, his Head Queen, the Most Beautiful Queen Balkis, was nearly as wise as he was.

Suleiman-bin-Daoud was strong. Upon the third finger of his right hand he wore a ring. When he turned it once, Afrits and Djinns came out of the earth to do whatever he told them.

And yet Suleiman-bin-Daoud was not proud. He very seldom showed off, and when he did he was sorry for it.

From JUST-SO STORIES, by Rudyard Kipling.

He married ever so many wives. He married nine hundred and ninety-nine wives, besides the Most Beautiful Balkis; and they all lived in a great golden palace in the middle of a lovely garden with fountains. He didn't really want nine hundred and ninety-nine wives, but in those days everybody married ever so many wives, and of course the King had to marry ever so many more just to show that he was the King.

Some of the wives were nice, but some were simply horrid, and the horrid ones quarrelled with the nice ones and made them horrid too, and then they would all quarrel with Suleiman-bin-Daoud, and that was horrid for him. But Balkis the Most Beautiful never quarrelled with Suleiman-bin-Daoud. She loved him too much. She sat in her rooms in the Golden Palace, or walked in the Palace garden, and was truly sorry for him.

Of course if he had chosen to turn his ring on his finger and call up the Djinns and the Afrits they would have magicked all those nine hundred and ninety-nine quarrelsome wives into white mules of the desert or greyhounds or pomegranate seeds; but Suleiman-bin-Daoud thought that that would be showing off. So, when they quarrelled too much, he only walked by himself in one part of the beautiful Palace gardens and wished he had never been born.

One day, when they had quarrelled for three weeks—all nine hundred and ninety-nine wives together—Suleiman-bin-Daoud went out for peace and quiet as usual; and among the orange-trees he met Balkis the Most Beautiful, very sorrowful because Suleiman-bin-Daoud was so worried.

And Balkis the Most Beautiful said, "O my Lord and Treasure of my Soul, what will you do?"

And Suleiman-bin-Daoud said, "O my Lady and Content of my Heart, I shall continue to endure my fate at the hands of these nine hundred and ninety-nine Queens who vex me with their continual quarrelling."

So he went on between the lilies and the loquats and the roses and the cannas and the heavy-scented ginger plants that grew in the garden, till he came to the great camphor tree that was called the Camphor Tree of Suleiman-bin-Daoud. But Balkis hid among the tall irises and the spotted bamboos and the red lilies behind the camphor tree, so as to be near her own true love, Suleiman-bin-Daoud.

Presently two Butterflies flew under the tree, quarrelling.

Suleiman-bin-Daoud heard one say to the other, "I wonder at your presumption in talking like this to me. Don't you know that if I stamped with my foot all Suleiman-bin-Daoud's Palace and this garden here would immediately vanish in a clap of thunder?"

Then Suleiman-bin-Daoud forgot his nine hundred and ninety-nine bothersome wives, and laughed, till the camphor tree shook, at the Butterfly's boast. And he held out his finger and said, "Little man, come here."

The Butterfly was dreadfully frightened, but he managed to fly up to the hand of Suleiman-bin-Daoud, and clung there, fanning himself. Suleiman-bin-Daoud bent his head and whispered very softly, "Little man, you know that all your stamping wouldn't bend one blade of grass. What made you tell that awful fib to your wife?—for doubtless she is your wife."

The Butterfly looked at Suleiman-bin-Daoud and saw the most wise King's eyes twinkle like stars on a frosty night, and he picked up his courage with both wings, and he put his head on one side and said, "O King, live for ever! She *is* my wife; and you know what wives are like."

Suleiman-bin-Daoud smiled in his beard and said, "Yes, *I* know, little brother."

"One must keep them in order somehow," said the Butterfly, "and she has been quarrelling with me all the morning. I said that to quiet her."

And Suleiman-bin-Daoud said, "May it quiet her. Go back to your wife, little brother, and let me hear what you say."

Back flew the Butterfly to his wife, who was all of a twitter behind a leaf, and she said, "He heard you! Suleiman-bin-Daoud himself heard you!"

"Heard me!" said the Butterfly. "Of course he did. I meant him to hear me."

"And what did he say? Oh, what did he say?"

"Well," said the Butterfly, fanning himself most importantly, "between you and me, my dear—of course I don't blame him, because his palace must have cost a great deal and the oranges are just ripening—he asked me not to stamp, and I promised I wouldn't."

"Gracious!" said his wife, and sat quite quiet; but Suleiman-bin-Daoud laughed till the tears ran down his face at the impudence of the bad little Butterfly.

Balkis the Most Beautiful stood up behind the tree among the red lilies and smiled to herself, for she had heard all this talk. She thought, "If I am wise I can yet save my Lord from the persecutions of these quarrelsome Queens," and she held out her finger and whispered softly to the Butterfly's Wife, "Little woman, come here."

Up flew the Butterfly's Wife, very frightened, and clung to Balkis's white hand.

Balkis bent her beautiful head down and whispered, "Little woman, do you believe what your husband has just said?"

The Butterfly's Wife looked at Balkis, and saw the Most Beautiful Queen's eyes shining like deep pools with starlight on them, and she picked up her courage with both wings and said, "O Queen, be lovely for ever. You know what menfolk are like."

"Little sister,'" said Balkis, "you are quite right; but next time he begins to boast, take him at his word. Ask him to stamp, and see what will happen. We know what menfolk are like, don't we? He'll be very much ashamed."

Away flew the Butterfly's Wife to her husband, and in five minutes they were quarrelling worse than ever.

"Remember!" said the Butterfly. "Remember what I can do if I stamp my foot."

"I don't believe you one little bit," said the Butterfly's Wife. "I should very much like to see it done. Suppose you stamp now."

"I promised Suleiman-bin-Daoud that I wouldn't," said the Butterfly, "and I don't want to break my promise."

"It wouldn't matter if you did," said his wife. "You couldn't bend a blade of grass with your stamping. I dare you to do it," she said. "Stamp! Stamp! Stamp!"

Suleiman-bin-Daoud, sitting under the camphor tree, heard

every word of this, and he laughed as he had never laughed in his life before. He forgot all about his Queens. He just laughed with joy, and Balkis, on the other side of the tree, smiled because her own true love was so joyful.

Presently the Butterfly, very hot and puffy, came whirling back under the shadow of the camphor tree and said to Suleiman, "She wants me to stamp! She wants to see what will happen, O Suleiman-bin-Daoud! You know I can't do it, and now she'll never believe a word I say. She'll laugh at me to the end of my days!"

"No, little brother," said Suleiman-bin-Daoud, "she will never laugh at you again," and he turned the ring on his finger—just for the little Butterfly's sake, not for the sake of showing off—and, lo and behold, four huge Djinns came out of the earth!

"Slaves," said Suleiman-bin-Daoud, "when this gentleman on my finger" (that was where the impudent Butterfly was sitting) "stamps his left front forefoot you will make my Palace and these gardens disappear in a clap of thunder. When he stamps again you will bring them back carefully."

"Now, little brother," he said, "go back to your wife and stamp all you've a mind to."

Away flew the Butterfly to his wife, who was crying, "I dare you to do it! I dare you to do it! Stamp! Stamp now! Stamp!" Balkis saw the four vast Djinns stoop down to the four corners of the gardens with the Palace in the middle, and she clapped her hands softly and said, "At last Suleiman-bin-Daoud will do for the sake of a Butterfly what he ought to have done long ago for his own sake, and the quarrelsome Queens will be frightened!"

Then the Butterfly stamped. The Djinns jerked the Palace and the gardens a thousand miles into the air: there was a most awful thunderclap, and everything grew inky-black. The Butterfly's Wife fluttered about in the dark, crying, "Oh, I'll be good! I'm so sorry I spoke! Only bring the gardens back, my dear darling husband, and I'll never contradict again."

The Butterfly was nearly as frightened as his wife, and Suleiman-bin-Daoud laughed so much that it was several minutes before he found breath enough to whisper to the Butterfly, "Stamp again, little brother. Give me back my Palace, most great magician."

So he stamped once more, and that instant the Djinns let down the Palace and the gardens, without even a bump. The sun shone on the dark-green orange-leaves; the fountains played among the pink Egyptian lilies; the birds went on singing; and the Butterfly's Wife lay on her side under the camphor tree waggling her wings and panting, "Oh, I'll be good! I'll be good!"

Suleiman-bin-Daoud could hardly speak for laughing. He leaned back all weak and hiccoughy, and shook his finger at the Butterfly and said, "O great wizard, what is the sense of returning to me my Palace if at the same time you slay me with mirth?"

Then came a terrible noise, for all the nine hundred and ninety-nine Queens ran out of the Palace shrieking and shouting and calling for their babies. They hurried down the great marble steps below the fountain, one hundred abreast, and the Most Wise Balkis went statelily forward to meet them and said, "What is your trouble, O Queens?"

They stood on the marble steps one hundred abreast and shouted, "What is our trouble? We were living peacefully in our golden Palace, as is our custom, when upon a sudden the Palace disappeared, and we were left sitting in a thick and noisome darkness; and it thundered, and Djinns and Afrits moved about in the darkness! That is our trouble, O Head Queen, and we are most extremely troubled on account of that trouble, for it was a troublesome trouble, unlike any trouble we have known."

Then Balkis the Most Beautiful Queen—Suleiman-bin-Daoud's Very Best Beloved—Balkis, almost as wise as the Most Wise Suleiman-bin-Daoud himself, said, "It is nothing, O Queens! A Butterfly has made complaint against his wife because she quarrelled with him, and it has pleased our Lord Suleiman-bin-Daoud to teach her a lesson in low-speaking and humbleness, for that is counted a virtue among the wives of the butterflies."

Then up and spoke an Egyptian Queen—the daughter of a Pharaoh—and she said, "Our Palace cannot be plucked up by the roots like a leek for the sake of a little insect. No! Suleiman-bin-Daoud must be dead, and what we heard and saw was the earth thundering and darkening at the news."

Then Balkis beckoned that bold Queen without looking at her, and said to her and to the others, "Come and see."

They came down the marble steps, one hundred abreast, and beneath his camphor tree, still weak with laughing, they saw the Most Wise King Suleiman-bin-Daoud rocking back and forth with a Butterfly on either hand, and they heard him say, "O wife of my brother in the air, remember after this to please your husband in all things, lest he be provoked to stamp his foot yet again; for he has said that he is used to this magic, and he is most eminently a great magician—one who steals away the very Palace of Suleiman-bin-Daoud himself. Go in peace, little folk!" And he kissed them on the wings, and they flew away.

Then all the Queens except Balkis—the Most Beautiful and Splendid Balkis, who stood apart smiling—fell flat on their faces, for they said, "If these things are done when a Butterfly is displeased with his wife, what shall be done to us who have vexed our King with our loud-speaking and open quarrelling through many days?"

Then they put their veils over their heads, and they put their hands over their mouths, and they tiptoed back to the Palace most mousy-quiet.

Then Balkis—the Most Beautiful and Excellent Balkis—went forward through the red lilies into the shade of the camphor tree and laid her hand upon Suleiman-bin-Daoud's shoulder and said, "O my Lord and Treasure of my Soul, rejoice, for we have taught the Queens of Egypt and Mesopotamia and Abyssinia and Persia and India and China with a great and a memorable teaching."

And Suleiman-bin-Daoud, still looking after the Butterflies where they played in the sunlight, said, "O my Lady and Jewel of my Felicity, when did this happen? For I have been jesting with a Butterfly ever since I came into the garden." And he told Balkis what he had done.

Balkis—the Tender and Most Lovely Balkis—said, "O my Lord and Regent of my Existence, I hid behind the camphor tree and saw it all. It was I who told the Butterfly's Wife to ask the Butterfly to stamp, because I hoped that for the sake of the jest my Lord would make some great Magic and that the Queens would see it and be frightened." And she told him what the Queens had said and seen and thought.

Then Suleiman-bin-Daoud rose up from his seat under the camphor tree, and stretched his arms and rejoiced and said, "O my Lady and Sweetener of my Days, know that if I had made a Magic against my Queens for the sake of pride or anger, I should certainly have been put to shame. But by means of your wisdom I made the Magic for the sake of a jest and for the sake of a little Buttterfly, and—behold—it has also delivered me from the vexations of my vexatious wives! Tell me, therefore, O my Lady and Heart of my Heart, how did you come to be so wise?"

And Balkis the Queen, beautiful and tall, looked up into Suleiman-bin-Daoud's eyes and put her head a little on one side, just like the Butterfly, and said, "First, O my Lord, because I loved you; and secondly, O my Lord, because I know what womenfolk are."

Then they went up to the Palace and lived happily ever afterwards.

But wasn't it clever of Balkis?

> There was never a Queen like Balkis,
> From here to the wide world's end;
> But Balkis talked to a butterfly
> As you would talk to a friend.
>
> There was never a King like Solomon,
> Not since the world began;
> But Solomon talked to a butterfly
> As a man would talk to a man.
>
> She was Queen of Sabaea—
> And he was Asia's Lord—
> But they both of 'em talked to butterflies
> When they took their walks abroad!

ELEANOR FARJEON

Queen Esther, Who Saved Her People

In the Bible, we read of Esther, who became wife of a Persian king and was able to prevent the wholesale massacre of the Jewish race within that empire. This is the story of how she saved her people because she was brave as well as beautiful. Esther was chosen as his queen by King Xerxes, who ruled from 486–465 B.C., after a beauty contest of maidens from villages and towns all over his vast domain.

THIS IS A TALE of the King with two names. One of his names was a very long name, Ahasuerus, by which he is called in the Bible. But in the stories of Ancient Greece, his name was Xerxes. Now listen.

From MIGHTY MEN, by Eleanor Farjeon.

Xerxes was a King in Asia, and he ruled over a hundred and twenty-seven countries, from the land of the brown-skinned Indians to the land of the black-skinned Negroes. He was rich and mighty, and proud of his riches, and he wanted everyone to admire him and his might, so he made a great feast for the nobles and the princes in all his countries; and when they came he showed them his riches, and asked all the people in, both great and small.

They had the feast in the court of the palace garden, with its pillars of marble, and curtains of white, green, and blue, with purple cords and silver rings; and the couches were of gold and silver, and the pavement was of colored marble, red, and blue, and white, and black. And there they sat and drank the King's wine from golden goblets.

On the seventh day of the feast the King was merry with drinking, and he said: "Let Vashti, my Queen, be sent for, that I may show her to the princes and the people in her beauty; for my other treasure they have seen, but she is the fairest of all."

But Queen Vashti was angry at being sent for to be made a show of, and refused to come.

Now the King had a black temper when he did not get his own way, and he cried:

"Vashti shall no longer be my Queen! I will send her away and choose another Queen from the fairest maidens in the land."

And he sent Vashti away, and messengers went forth bidding all the loveliest maidens in the city to come before the King.

The loveliest of all was a young Jewess called Esther, who lived with her cousin, Old Mordecai the Jew. There were many Jews living here and there in the land, but the other people did not like them, and treated them badly. So when Esther's time came to go before the King, Mordecai advised her not to let him know she was a Jewess; and she did as he advised. She was so beautiful that the King loved her better than any of the others and made her his Queen. But nobody knew that Queen Esther was a Jewess. And her old cousin Mordecai sat humbly at the King's gate, and watched her pass in and out of the palace.

As he sat there, he heard talk of the people who went in and out; and one day two of the King's servants whispered together that they meant to kill the King. The next time Esther passed, Mordecai stood up in the gate and told her; and Queen Esther told the King how Mordecai had overheard the plot, and the King had the two servants hanged on a tree.

Now the King had among his courtiers a favorite whose name was Haman, and no one hated the Jews so much as Haman did. The King gave Haman great honors and ordered that all his servants should bow whenever he went by. But when Haman went in and out of the King's gate, Mordecai never bowed; he just sat where he was. Then Haman was angry; he knew Mordecai was a Jew, and he thought of a plan to punish all the Jews, and Mordecai among them. So he went to the King and said:

"There are certain people, called Jews, who have no country of their own, but are scattered here and there through all your countries; but they have their own laws, and do not obey yours, and it would be better for you not to keep them. So send forth papers saying they must all be killed, and I will myself give you ten thousand talents of silver to pay for the killing."

And the King gave his ring to Haman, for that was the sign of his power, and told him to write out the papers saying the Jews must all be killed on the thirteenth day of the twelfth month. Haman sent the papers into all the King's countries, sealed with the King's ring; and the Jews read how they were to be killed when the day came. But Queen Esther, inside the palace, knew nothing of the danger to her own people.

Then Mordecai, who had read the paper, dressed himself in sackcloth and poured ashes on his head and went through the city with a loud and bitter cry till he came to the King's gate; and he sent in word to Esther of the plot, and bade her beg the King to save the Jews, who were her own people.

And Esther said, "I may not go to the King unless he sends for me; for it is the Law that anyone who approaches the King of his own accord must die, unless the King holds out his golden sceptre towards him. But I will take the risk. I will go to the King, though he has not sent for me; and if I die, I die."

Then Esther put on her royal robes, and went to the King's

house; and when the King saw her standing so beautiful in his court he was pleased with her, and held out his golden sceptre, and said:

"What wilt thou, Queen Esther, and what is thy request? It shall be even given to thee to the half of my kingdom."

And Esther said, "I beg that the King and Haman will come tonight to the banquet I have prepared."

So that night the King and Haman supped with Queen Esther, and as they sat drinking, the King asked again: "What wilt thou, Queen Esther, and what is thy request? Even to the half of my kingdom, it is thine."

But Esther only said, "I beg that the King and Haman will sup with me again tomorrow night."

And Haman went away puffed up with pride, because he alone had been asked to sup twice with the King and Queen. And he had a gallows built ready to hang Mordecai, fifty cubits high.

Now that night as the King was looking through some papers, he found one telling how Mordecai had once saved him from a plot, and he thought, "Mordecai saved my life, yet I have done him no honor for it." And he sent at once for Haman and asked him, "What shall be done to the man whom the King delights to honor?"

Then Haman thought in his heart: "The King must mean me!" And he said, "The King's own clothes should be put on that man, and the King's crown on his head, and he should ride on the King's own horse through the city, and the noblest prince should go before him crying, 'This is the man the King delights to honor!'"

Then the King said, "Mordecai is the man; do all this as you have said, and ride before him yourself through the city, crying that he is the man I delight to honor."

And Haman was full of shame and anger, but he had to do it, while Mordecai rode through the city on the King's horse, wearing the King's crown.

When it was done, Mordecai sat once more in the King's gate, but Haman hurried to his own house, full of anger.

Then came the second night when the King and Haman

supped with Queen Esther. And as they sat at supper the King said, "What wilt thou, Queen Esther, and what is thy request? Let it be even the half of my kingdom!"

Then Esther knelt before the King and said: "O King, I beg of you my life, and the life of my people, for we have an enemy who wants to kill us."

And the King said, "Who is the enemy that dares do this to thee?"

And Esther answered, "He is this wicked Haman!"

The King was so full of wrath that he sprang up and walked in the garden, and there he saw over the wall the tall gallows which Haman had built the day before.

He asked a servant, "What is that?" And the servant said, "It is the gallows Haman built for Mordecai, who saved the King's life."

Then the King said, "Hang Haman on it!"

So they hanged Haman on his own gallows, fifty cubits high. And the King sent for Mordecai to come into the palace, and he gave him his own ring, which he had taken from Haman, and made him next to himself in power over the people.

PUT ON YOUR PURPLE, ESTHER

by ELEANOR FARJEON

Put on your purple, Esther, Esther;
Esther, put on your crown of gold,
And go and wait
By the King's own gate—
For your people will perish, Esther, Esther,
Unless your heart is bold!

She put on her purple and crown, did Esther;
Esther she did as she was told.
She broke the Law,
But the King, who saw,
Said, "She is beautiful, Esther, Esther!"
And held out his rod of gold.

IRIS NOBLE

Cleopatra

Cleopatra has gripped the imagination of novelists, playwrights, poets, and historians all through the ages. Though the historical facts are well known, the personality behind them emerges differently for different people. In the following pages, the novelist, Iris Noble, pictures Cleopatra, just before she came to the throne of Egypt in the year 51 B.C.

"DEMETRIUS, what do these words mean—filial love?"

As she asked the question the girl looked up from the papyrus scroll she was studying. She leaned her elbows on the yellow and white alabaster table and cupped her chin in her hands. Hopefully, she scrutinized the face of her teacher.

Demetrius pulled at his white, curly beard before he answered. "Princess Cleopatra, surely that is a simple term to understand? Filial is the relationship of son or daughter to parent. Love—cannot you define love?"

She moved, impatiently. Her long, coppery-brown hair lay unbound around her shoulders. She tossed it back out of her eyes. "I know what filial means and I know the definition of love.

From EGYPT'S QUEEN, CLEOPATRA, by Iris Noble.

My father is Auletes, Ptolemy the Eleventh. I am Cleopatra, his daughter. That is our relationship. But when poets and philosophers speak of filial love, filial duty, filial respect as being so very important I am not sure that I know their full meaning. They are just words to me."

"I cannot believe you speak seriously," Demetrius said. "I—"

Sosigenes, the astronomer, interrupted him. "How can she be expected to know? In this room I speak plainly." His voice was harsh. "Has she ever known the love of a parent?" He looked around at the other three teachers and then down at the slight figure of the thirteen-year-old girl. "Her mother is dead. Her father is a drunkard and a spendthrift and a fool, in debt to Romans who laugh at his antics, loan him money so that they can keep him prisoner in Rome until they decide what to do with us. How can the Princess be expected to feel love or respect or duty toward him?"

"Love and respect toward one's parents," objected the quiet Josephus, the Jewish teacher of languages, "is a natural impulse of the human being. A family is not a family without the emotions which bind parents and children together. Is there nothing in your heart, child, for your father Auletes?"

"I feel sorry for him," she said, groping for the right way to express her vague emotions. "It is wrong for Berenice to try to take the throne away from him. She is wicked. My father is king, even if he is everything Sosigenes says of him. I will do whatever I can to help him. Is that loving him?"

She looked at the four of them in turn. Sosigenes had said that in this room he spoke plainly. It was so. When she had first come to the great museum to study she had been eleven and undisciplined. No slave or servant or attendant had ever argued with her or told her unpleasant truths. She had been startled that these scholars sought for reality, no matter how distasteful. She was furious when they said her reasoning might be wrong or faulty.

She made scenes. She called them names. She cried, stormed, ordered them to admit that a royal princess could not be wrong. They had been firm. Josephus had spoken for all of them when he told her, gently: "We risk our lives in letting you come here.

Do not ask us to risk what is more precious to us than our lives: honor, truth, integrity."

That had been two years ago. She was glad they had fought her. She had learned to face facts; own up to her errors; and value this hard, constant search for exactness in what was known and for logical theories of what was not known.

The room had become for her and for them a place where they might speak freely. It was a small room, beautiful with its white stone pillars, its lofty ceiling and the open window which looked out to the harbor of Alexandria. It was a hidden room. Few people found their way there. Students and teachers and research scholars were familiar with the other, larger rooms in this vast building, but this one was known to only a few.

The Museum and Library of Alexandria was famous. Around it a great university had sprung up. The most renowned teachers came here. Among them, these four—Demetrius, Josephus, Sosigenes, and old Serapion—were Cleopatra's friends.

Surely these men could help her solve the riddle of her strange life? "I think I feel pity," she continued her thoughts, "but not love. I do not think I have ever felt love. What is it?"

Sosigenes exploded, "Josephus, you say it is a natural impulse to love. How can a natural impulse grow in an unnatural family? The Ptolemies are cursed. Father has slain daughter, brother poisoned sister, wife killed husband, mothers destroyed their own children, for more than a hundred years. That is their history. You know it as well as I. This Greek family of the Ptolemy, who have ruled Egypt for centuries, have had no concept of love. They hate. They lust. They scheme. They kill. They do not love."

"Does that mean a Ptolemy cannot?" Josephus' hand fell kindly on Cleopatra's shoulder. "This one has intelligence."

Sosigenes stood his ground. "I am speaking of what goes on inside the royal palace. I am warning you, Princess, so you will not be like the others. The spilling of blood is not unique to the Ptolemies. Other royal families have murdered when it suited them, but the Ptolemies have long ago forgotten what it is to love."

Tiny, elderly, wrinkled Serapion, the mathematician, had been quietly rocking in his corner, taking no part in the discussion. Now he spoke. "How can the child forget what she does not know? Josephus' wisdom and Sosigenes' shouting won't teach it to her. She pities her father. That is a good start. Nurture that feeling, Princess. But now get on with your studies and let an old man have peace to do his mathematical calculations."

The room was quiet. Only the rustle of the papyrus pages, the scratch of stylus pens, the low murmur of the voices of Cleopatra and Josephus were heard.

Suddenly the door opened. Cleopatra looked up, startled. Where was the slave who was supposed to guard that door against intruders?

Two young men lounged in the open doorway, leisurely looking about them. "There is nothing here, Titus," one said. "It must be simply a retreat for these old scholars."

"You are right." They both spoke Greek but this one had the accent of a Roman. "There is nothing here. Besides, I am fatigued. We have been an entire day strolling through this museum. Tomorrow I begin my studies. I swear by Venus that I have been less tired in a chariot race in Rome than in visiting all these halls and rooms, these libraries, these dining halls and galleries. Who but these decadent Alexandrians would put so much money into books and learning—wait! Did you say there was nothing here? Do you see what I do? A young female in a place of study; this is incredible."

The situation appealed to Cleopatra's sense of humor. She put her hand on Josephus' arm as he started to rise and silence the two insolent young men. It was she who rose and walked timidly across the room to the door.

"My lords," she said, letting her hair hang down over her face and lowering her eyes demurely, "good masters, do not disturb the wise scholars. You think it strange that I am here? Cannot even old men have young slave girls to fetch and carry the papyrus scrolls for them?"

"Shocking," said the one called Titus. "I have heard stories of the strange customs of these people, but for learned men to coddle themselves with the services of a slave girl is worse than I thought. Come away," he said.

When they were gone and Cleopatra closed the door, she leaned her head on it and laughed.

"You have caused a scandal," reproved Demetrius.

"You should not have said that. It was a falsehood," said Josephus.

"You behaved most unbecoming a modest girl and a princess," admonished Sosigenes.

Suddenly from old Serapion came a wheeze and a choke and a gurgle and then a burst of snickers and titters. It was too much for the other teachers, and they, too, began to laugh. Cleopatra fell onto a bench and rocked her small body back and forth, holding onto her sides. "It is so good," she gasped out, finally, "to laugh. I so seldom have the chance. Forgive me."

Sosigenes wiped his eyes. "If the truth be admitted, Princess, I think we old men welcome your presence here as much for such pranks as for our pride in having such a brilliant student." His face grew sober. "Come, back to your lessons. You have much to learn."

The shadows in the small, secret room grew long. Cleopatra rolled up the scroll she was studying and sighed. It was time to return to the palace.

Her slave awaited her outside the door. "You left your post this afternoon," she said, angrily.

"Forgive me, Princess," he begged. "I thought I had a chance to learn some news for you. You ordered me to listen when I heard anything of Rome."

"What did you hear?" She followed him to a private side door.

"I could not understand it. They were new students from Rome, and they talked a lot about a man named Caesar. I did not understand. I thought it was a man called Pompey who was king—"

"You are stupid," she said. "They do not have kings. They elect consuls. Pompey has been the great one as long as I remember. I don't know this Caesar, except that he was the general who stole Cyprus. I hope Pompey kills him."

"The students said Pompey and Caesar were friends—" The slave began to speak but she hushed him. They were outside. She drew a cloak around her which concealed all of her, including her head. She stepped into a litter, which was hoisted to the shoulders of four slaves. Through a curtain in it she could see out, but not be seen.

They went past the Museum and Library, the theater, and the Temple of Pan. Across the street, between warehouses, she caught glimpses of the harbor. There were dozens of ships in it—galleys, trading vessels, triremes, small pleasure boats. Goods were being ferried to and from the docks.

She was carried past piled sacks of rice and grain from the Nile Valley. Her litter dodged the long human chain of workmen and slaves who lined the quay, passing boxes and sacks from one to another. She could smell pitch and tar from the boats; wine in casks; spices from the East; the rich fragrance of fruit.

Along the harbor sauntered the merchants and traders. Beggars followed them, whining for coins, ready to run at the approach of a harbor guard.

A chariot rattled over the stones. "Give way!" cried the charioteer. Cleopatra's slaves moved hastily to one side to avoid being hit by the two charging horses. She saw Achillas, the best Egyptian general, standing upright in the chariot. He was an arrogant man, this Achillas, she thought. He would bear watching.

Then she was through the gates of the palace. Just inside was a long, palm-shaded pavilion. It was a favorite with the aristocrats of Alexandria who came there to exchange gossip. The litter which bore Cleopatra went slowly here. Her slaves had orders not to push their way through or call attention to themselves. Also, going slowly she could look and listen. Sometimes she heard things she could convey by secret messenger to her father.

Two wealthy matrons were talking about fashion when they were joined by a man. He was Pothinus. Cleopatra's brother Ptolemy was in his charge, but he had made himself more important than that position warranted. Though he had neither rank nor wealth he was recognized as a force in the palace. He had his ways of knowing things before others did.

Cleopatra shifted her body to the right. Her slaves knew her silent commands and they also went to the right, close to the group where Pothinus was. She wanted to hear better. It was difficult because Pothinus was whispering. She could only hear: ". . . at last . . . Berenice sent . . . it is true . . . envoys to Rome with . . . don't ask me how much . . . a fortune, perhaps. . . ."

She had heard enough. With shaking hands she rapped three times. Her slaves went faster, hurrying around people, rushing along the pavilion paths.

It wasn't fast enough for her. She murmured, even though they couldn't hear her, "Hurry! Run—I may be too late!"

The whispered words had been clear to her. Berenice had at last sent her official envoys to Rome to insist upon her recognition as queen. They would go with an enormous fortune to bribe the Romans. Cleopatra must get word to her father at once.

As soon as she was in her own apartments she commanded Charmian, her attendant: "Go to the outer pavilion. Bring Appolodorus to me instantly, but let no one see you do it."

She could trust Appolodorus. He had acted as go-between before, bringing her messages that sea captains had slipped to him, from her father in Rome. While she waited for him she wrote the letter and sealed it and had it ready when the young man entered.

"Do you know of a captain willing to take chances?" she asked, handing him the letter. "One who will get the utmost speed from his ship and race the envoys of Berenice to Rome? The envoys must have left last night or this morning."

"This morning; Pothinus said so." Appolodorus' handsome face looked as carefree and thoughtless as that of any other young Alexandrian of the fashionable class, but he had a rare and steadfast loyalty to both the King and this daughter. "There is one captain who might be persuaded to sail tonight and work his galley slaves hard, if he is paid well. He will want payment in advance—a lot of it."

Cleopatra left him for a second and came back with her jewel case. Diamonds and rubies which had once been her mother's she now gave to him. "Bargain with him as best you can but let not a single jewel stand in the way of success."

Appolodorus bowed and left.

Weeks of anxiety and tension went by. The whole palace felt it. By turns, Berenice seemed to be riding the crest of confidence that she would be queen, or screaming at her attendants and advisers when her nerves became fearful. More than ever Cleopatra tried to stay away from her. She came back from the library much later than before and stayed hidden in her own rooms and gardens.

One evening, late, she and Charmian and Iras were in her small garden by the lotus pool. Palm trees were graceful shapes in the twilight. The air was still warm.

Both Charmian and Iras were maidens of noble family. They were in-waiting on the Princess, but because all three were so much the same age they were more friends than attendants. Charmian pulled a lotus flower out of the pool and held it in her cupped hands. Iras had placed a lump of scented oil on the top of her curls, in the Egyptian custom, and was enjoying the sweetness and coolness of it as it melted and ran down her cheeks.

Cleopatra sat on a bench a little distant from them. Behind her was a thick fig tree, and all around her hung grapes from a trellis. Back of the fig tree was a low wall supporting open stone grillwork.

The two girls were playing their favorite game while she listened. It was called "if Cleopatra were queen—"

"If you were queen, Cleopatra, I think you should forbid anyone in the palace eating onions. Berenice must adore them. The smell comes up from the kitchens. It is horrible."

"If you were queen, Cleopatra, you could pass for the goddess Isis. Your features are Grecian but you are shaped like an Egyptian. You are slim."

"Shall I show you how Berenice looks?" Cleopatra darted a quick glance about her, then stood up and postured before the other girls. She was a superb mimic. Her shoulders slumped and seemed to grow thick; her legs waddled as though they held much weight. She scowled.

"So—!" The child who had come stealthily into the garden surprised them all. "This is the way you mock our beloved older sister? What will you give me not to tell?" She had the face of a child but the eyes of a strange and cruel animal.

"I give you nothing, Arsinoë. You are not wanted here. Go back to your own rooms." Cleopatra held her voice steady but her heart was pounding. There was something wrong, something unhealthy about Arsinoë. She might tell Berenice, just for spite. Or she might not tell, for her own sly reasons which no one could guess.

"I shall go where I please and do as I please. I am not the danger to Berenice that you are. I am only ten and you are now fourteen. Even if they decide she is to be queen, she won't like you. Ganymede says that someday you might be a challenge to Berenice." Ganymede was her tutor. He was as mean and spiteful as Arsinoë. Cleopatra disliked them both.

"Go away," she said, in quick anger, to Arsinoë. "You would be welcome to stay if you behaved nicely but I don't trust you."

She sat down on the bench and heard a faint rustle behind her. She froze like a statue, averting her head so that Arsinoë would not see her expression. The faintest of whispers reached her: "Princess—"

Without moving her lips she whispered back: "Wait. Say nothing." She watched Arsinoë dawdling by the pool; saw her rip up water lilies wantonly and tear them to pieces while she laughed at Charmian's protest. Would her sister never go? Cleopatra was in agony. She knew who the whisperer was and what it meant.

At last Arsinoë threw the lilies, with their muddy roots, into Charmian's face and ran off. While Iras was helping Charmian clean the dirt off, Cleopatra whispered, "Now—speak. It is safe. But softly so the maids do not hear." She trusted them, but if Berenice suspected anything she could torture information from them.

"Princess," came the whisper, "your father received the information you sent. Do you hear? He received it in time. He acted promptly. The envoys were seized when they landed and were killed before they could speak for Berenice. Your father took the money they had. He paid some of his debts."

"Yes. Go on. Quickly," she urged.

"The King made bold to press his claims to the Roman Senate. The wheel of fortune turned. Julius Caesar stood up and declared Auletes was the rightful king and that Egypt is an ally of Rome. I was told to repeat that: an ally of Rome."

The whisper stopped and she pleaded, "Is there no more?"

"Nothing, Princess. I must go." There was the tiniest rustle of leaves behind her, then there was silence. She got up, slowly. The rustle began again and she sank back on the bench.

"Forgive me," came the whisper again. "I am stupid. I forget the most important news. The Roman proconsul of Syria, one Gabinius, is desperate for our Egyptian gold to pay his soldiers there. Your father has offered him six thousand talents of gold from the royal treasury if Gabinius will march here with his legions and put Auletes back on the throne."

"Has Gabinius agreed?" she asked.

"I do not know," he said.

Though she waited a while, this time the whispering messenger had come to the end of his information. There was no further sound behind her.

Dangerous as it was both for him and for her, she must see Appolodorus. She met him in her study room in the museum. The old scholars were discreetly absent. She told the young man the news.

"Does this mean that my father is once more rightful king and that Berenice is declared a usurper?" she asked him.

Appolodorus was even more excited than she. "It means more than that. I have been hearing more rumors about this Caesar. He and Pompey and a rich man, Crassus, have been named as a triumvirate to control all Rome and its colonies. Their term is limited by the Senate, but in fact they rule. They are supposed to be good friends but there is suspicion among the three."

What Rome did or did not do was unimportant to Cleopatra. "Will my father come? Do you think this Gabinius will accept his offer?"

"I don't know but we must be ready. Berenice will be a mad dog when she hears this. Eat no food that a slave has not already tested for poison. I know a loyal army captain. He will loan me four or five fighting men. We will dress them as slaves, smuggle them into your rooms, and they will guard every entrance day and night."

"Will you warn Pothinus so he can guard my brother?" She was trying not to be afraid but she was shivering.

Appolodorus' eyebrows went up. "Pothinus? He undoubtedly knows more than we, Cleopatra."

For more than two weeks she was guarded. She never left her rooms. Iras reported that Berenice's supporters had stopped coming to the palace. Servants gossiped in corners. The kitchens were in turmoil. Twice there was no hot water for Cleopatra's baths. Even when she slept she was aware of the restless prowling of her guards, and once she heard a scuffle. "What is it?" She crept to the door.

"A visitor, Princess. The ruffian had a knife. I broke his arm. Go back to sleep, please. I taught him a lesson," said the gruff soldier.

With a Roman army clearing the way for him and with the Roman general Gabinius leading the campaign, Auletes, Ptolemy XI, came home to Alexandria in triumph. It was a short and easy victory. The half-hearted opposition was swept away.

When the best Egyptian general, Achillas, went over to the side of the king with his army, Berenice was caught in a trap. Achillas was in Alexandria and he knew just who had favored her cause. He crushed them and went out of the gates to join the onmarching Gabinius.

Inside the palace all was confusion. When the Roman trumpets could be heard outside the palace walls, Cleopatra refused to stay in her rooms any longer. With her guards as protection and with Charmian and Iras following, she walked out into the lofty white stone halls. Some seemed deserted but in one great audience chamber she found throngs of the wealthy Alexandrian aristocrats.

They were frightened. Hands clutched at her. "Remember,

Princess Cleopatra, that we never liked Berenice. . . ."

"My husband was forced into her Council—he was forced. . . ."

"We were your friends. . . ."

"Don't let those Romans use their swords on us. They are beasts, we hear. . . ."

She was only fourteen. She was astounded at their behavior. Were they such cowards? Did they think she had the power to help them?

Pothinus was by her side. He was a huge, fat man, whose smile was as oily as the grease he used on his hair. "Princess Cleopatra, may I have a word with you?"

"Speak. You have permission." Even his manner had changed and he was obsequious to her. It puzzled Cleopatra.

"I have labored," his tone was humble but his eyes were not. They were bold. "I have labored day and night these past days to bring the banquet hall and the audience chamber into such suitable elegance as will welcome our great Ptolemy and his Roman friends. I would not have these Roman barbarians think we have some rude court. The kitchens were disorganized but I now have ready the finest wines, the meats, the fruits for the homecoming banquet. Magicians and musicians and dancing girls are hired for entertainment. The throne room is hung with new golden curtains."

Grudgingly, she had to say, "You have worked wonders, Pothinus."

"There is one thing more. All of Alexandria will be showering gifts on the King to show loyalty. Of course, Ptolemy has no reason to doubt his daughter, and I hope you will assure him he has had no reason to dislike me, Pothinus. But there is a gift I could give him—it will need your permission—" he hesitated.

"What is it?" she asked.

"The head of Berenice." He hurried to explain, as if he had to urge this thing, "She is hiding in her chambers. Her guards have deserted her. We run no danger from her. It would be easy."

"No! You would not kill her when she was a powerful danger to the King. Now when she is helpless—no, Pothinus, let my father do what he pleases." She turned away from the frustrated anger in his face. She knew he was furious because he had hoped to make himself a prominent favorite of the King's with this bloody act.

She was saved further argument from him by the rush of people to windows and doors. Drums, trumpets and pipes could be heard at the gates. The King and the Romans were here.

When Auletes, Ptolemy XI, mounted the steps of his palace the first person he saw waiting for him at the top was his daughter Cleopatra. Courtiers lined the enormous entrance hall but she alone stood in the center of it, waiting, thrilled and excited, ready to welcome him with love.

He embraced her, casually.

"Welcome, my father," she said. She looked up at his face.

What she saw shocked her. Weak tears of joy ran down his bloated, red-veined cheeks. His arm around her shoulder had no tenderness. He was smiling but not for her. He was saying, "At last! If you only knew what I have suffered—but it is all over. I am home. Faugh! You cannot imagine what it is like to live in an army tent. I am filthy. I want a bath. Stewards, take these gallant Roman officers to their apartments, but first send my musicians in so they may play for me while I bathe."

She stood and watched as he and the big mailed and helmeted figures of the Romans went down the hall. Her head drooped. Filial love—how could she feel love for this father? During the past year her imagination had dignified his memory a little. Now she knew he was still Auletes—the nickname so mockingly given him—"the Fluteplayer."

In the days and months that passed, life in the palace reverted to the way it had been when Cleopatra was a child. The Roman officers left. Two of their legions remained to help Auletes in case of trouble, but there was no trouble. Auletes permitted his advisers to do as they pleased, so long as they did not interfere with his fun. The palace was once again full of his old roistering, drunken, pleasure-loving companions.

Only Cleopatra was unhappy. She watched and observed. She could not forget how much more kingly the Romans had appeared than Auletes. She wondered who was actually running the affairs of Egypt. Since she could no longer go to the museum —Auletes had been shocked at her request—she found life dull and heavy.

Though Auletes usually ignored his children, he did notice her unhappy face. "Why do you not smile?" he demanded, fretfully. "Your manner annoys me. After all I have suffered, must I come back to your frowns and pouts? Your sister Arsinoë is amusing and gay. She pleases me more than you do."

The hint was very clear. It shocked Cleopatra into action. Auletes was shallow and so fickle that he might easily set her aside and name Arsinoë as his heir to the throne if Cleopatra offended him. She must do something to win back his favor.

She was not yet fifteen. She had no one to constantly urge her forward, as Theodotus and Pothinus did the young Ptolemy, or as Ganymede did for Arsinoë. This was her own fault. She had refused, when still a child, to be led around by such men nor could she be fooled by their flattery.

After a week of worrying, she made up her mind what she must do. Appolodorus and Olympus must help her. She summoned them, along with Iras and Charmian.

"It is time," she told them, "that I stop being the student and take my place in the society of the palace. I am ignorant of fashionable life. I plan to give a party and invite my father and all of Alexandria's aristocracy to it, so that they may begin to know me as their future queen."

Olympus, the physician, smiled at such pretentious words from such a young girl, but Appolodorus was more worldly. His eyes sparkled. He said, "Excellent! I can tell you that the Alexandrian nobles grumble. Auletes prefers his drunken rascals to them. They feel snubbed and shut out of the palace life. Would you hold the party here, Cleopatra? Then you must redecorate. These rooms have not been changed since your nursery days."

She looked about her and nodded. Iras and Charmian were excited. "You go to all the wealthy homes, Appolodorus," Charmian said. "You can advise us. Is there a particularly beautiful one we can copy?"

"No." Cleopatra was determined. "I will not follow fashion.

I will set it. I must startle everyone, including Auletes. I cannot be just another rich girl. A princess is expected to be different. I overheard some ladies talking one day about fashions. They said it was now smart to adapt a little of the old Egyptian style to our Grecian art. So I shall decorate these rooms completely Egyptian, as in the days of the Pharaohs. I shall dress, for the time being, as the Egyptians dressed."

"No white robes? No chitons? Are you not going to do your hair up in the Grecian style?" Iras was astounded.

But now that she knew what she wanted, Cleopatra's mind worked like lightning. "Appolodorus, scour the city for craftsmen who still work in the old manner, or find modern ones who will imitate the art of the Third Dynasty. Iras, call the best tailors and seamstresses. Charmian, I wish to speak with the head gardener. I want the best goldsmiths and silverworkers and sculptors here, today."

Appolodorus was enthusiastic. "There is a new shipment of copper objects in the harbor today. The Thos family has offered a large sum for just one copper screen, inlaid with pearls and malachite."

"Outbid them, Appolodorus," Cleopatra ordered recklessly.

"The most clever seamstress is a slave belonging to Rebecca, wife of Benjamin, the shipowner," said Charmian.

"Buy that slave at any price."

"But, child, where will you get the money for all this," Olympus objected. "Your father is too greedy to be lavish with you. His own expenditures are already causing murmurs throughout the city."

Cleopatra had already considered this. "Have you seen the petitioners crowding around the palace gate? Everyone wants something: a permit to unload at a better wharf; a pardon for a son taken in crime; a trading concession with our Nubian chiefs. Spread the word, Appolodorus, but quietly, that I have the ear of the King. They must apply to me. I will see they are heard without delay. That is all I will promise them—that they be heard—but they must pay me."

Olympus raised his eyebrows. "That is a common practice but

not by a girl of fourteen. You will antagonize some of the King's councilors who consider these bribes as belonging to them."

"I cannot help that." She was learning to be ruthless when it was necessary. "I cannot please everyone. At the moment, it is most important that I please my father."

"Then may I make a suggestion?" said Olympus. "Your father's eye may be pleased at new decorations, but he is more interested in music. You cannot, in modesty, provide him with the riotous entertainment he is accustomed to, but it would be refreshing and different if you turned one of your gardens into an aviary, with sweet-singing birds."

Impulsively, she went to him, clasped his arm and laid her head on his shoulder. "Thank you, Olympus."

It took time to accomplish all she wanted. She kept her preparations as secret as possible, but all day long her apartments were crowded with seamstresses, tailors, curtain-makers, painters, cabinetmakers, artists and artisans of all kinds. A hundred new gardeners were employed. Masons, tile-setters, bricklayers were in and out of her rooms.

Even before her party, she taught herself to smile at her father and laugh at his jokes. When she asked him to hear the petition of this man or that one, he grumbled but agreed. Money came easily to Cleopatra.

And, oddly, her mercenary motives brought her an unlooked-for reward. Listening to the petitioners' troubles taught her things about her own country she had not known before. A reservoir in Upper Egypt needed to be repaired? She was puzzled. She wondered why reservoirs were necessary. A caravan traveling through the desert had been taxed when they reached Memphis —did tax collectors have this right? The papyrus reeds in Lake Mareotis were growing too thickly, and the boats going to and from the Nile were becoming enmeshed in them. Should they not be cut down?

She caught a glimpse of the thousands of problems that could beset the ruler of such a country.

Great was the astonishment in the palace when announcement was made of an afternoon's entertainment in Princess Cleopatra's apartments. The tongues clacked loudly throughout the whole city. Some thought it was time for her to emerge into court society; some thought it presumption in one so young. All were curious and hoped for invitations.

When the afternoon arrived and she received her guests, their astonishment knew no bounds. Instead of the usual cool, chaste white rooms of Grecian art and architecture, with subdued lights and graceful pillars, these rooms were alive with color—reds, blues, greens, gold and silver—in the old Egyptian manner. Along the white walls were painted murals of Egyptian gods and kings and all phases of life—boats, rivers, trees and animals—in vivid colors. The figures were sharply etched in profile.

Golden lions in alabaster crouched holding up tables, chairs and couches. The Doric pillars had been painted over, in gold leaf and vermilion.

The lotus-flower and the papyrus motifs were everywhere— carved in precious stones, outlined in enamel work, fashioned into cups and in jars where rare incense burned.

The floor of her anteroom had been painted to resemble a fish pond so that her guests marveled as they seemed to walk over the water. The painted reeds seemed to bend under their feet. The fish and ducks were so realistic that many guests bent down to touch and feel them.

Couches, chairs and benches were carved out of solid ivory. The cushions on them were of gold silk. One table was made entirely of lapis lazuli; another of malachite. The copper screen which Appolodorus had bought for her stood behind a great alabaster vase.

"How exotic! How bizarre!" the guests murmured.

Most sensational of all was the Princess herself. While the other women and girls came in long robes gathered at the waist with crossed ribbons, Cleopatra was dressed in a tight sheath which covered her from above the breast straight to her ankles. It was tight and she was slim; in it she was a sculptured figure much like those of her wall paintings.

Her bronze-colored hair hung to her shoulders, curled in long ringlets, and over it she wore a diadem of gold, inset with green and red jewels. Around her neck was an extremely wide band which was also of gold and inset with pearls and rubies and green stones.

Since early morning she had been getting ready. She had been bathed and oiled. The manicurist and the chiropodist had been there. It had taken two hours to curl her hair, then her face was made up: green malachite eye shadow was applied to her upper lids and black kohl outlined the eyes and eyebrows to make them larger. Her nails were brushed with henna to pinken them and her lips painted with red.

"She is not as pretty as Arsinoë," Cleopatra heard one woman say, "but she does have distinction. An interesting face."

This they said when they thought she did not hear. Openly they said, "Dear little Princess Cleopatra, how charming you look. What a pleasure it is to feel the palace once more has a hostess! You have dazzled us all with this change; we must go home and redecorate in the Egyptian style. That copper screen— the Thos family must be eaten up with envy! The paintings are exquisite. I always thought of them as belonging in temples, not in homes, but of course a princess may do as she sees fit. . . ." On and on the voices babbled around her.

She kept herself aloof and dignified, although it was an effort. She was excited. When her father arrived, with his courtiers, she bowed to him and was pleased by his amazed delight. She conducted him, with all the guests trailing after, to the garden where thousands of birds in cages burst into song.

She did not have dancing girls or the kind of entertainers who sang doubtful jokes, but she did have a magician who was new to the palace and to Alexandria. Everyone was enchanted with the miracles he performed. He worked with birds, both live ones and toy ones, so that the whole afternoon seemed to be one of fairy enchantment.

It was suited to a young girl. The jaded appetites and tastes of the King and the Alexandrians were refreshed by it.

"I was wrong," Appolodorus whispered to her, "when I argued with you that this would be too tame and childish for them. They are enjoying the novelty of its innocence."

The party was a success. Auletes beamed upon her and called

her his favorite daughter, his lotus flower, his jewel. Arsinoë burst into tears and had to be taken out by her tutor, Ganymede. Saat, one of the King's advisers, noted for his honesty and his stiff-necked pride, spoke to Cleopatra.

He was a member of one of the oldest and noblest Egyptian families who looked upon the Greeks as interlopers, but he said to her, "You do yourself and your country great credit, Princess Cleopatra, in rediscovering the charm of Egyptian art and style. It becomes you."

"I like it, my lord Saat," she replied. "While I am proud of the Greek culture I never forget that this is Egypt."

"Then may I take advantage of my years and venture a criticism? We Egyptians like color and richness but, while your rooms are lovely, they are a bit too colorful and too rich," he said.

She was almost angry, then she looked into his wise, steady eyes and she blushed. "I will learn, my lord Saat."

He patted her arm, and she knew she had made a good friend.

When her father and the other guests left, she was surprised to find that Pothinus and General Achillas, who was now general of all the army, lingered behind.

"May we have a word with you in private, Princess?" Achillas asked.

"Of course," she said, leading the way to chairs for them. She was puzzled. Neither of these two had ever paid her much attention, and all of Pothinus' interest had been centered on her brother. Both were ambitious men. What did they want of her?

Pothinus began, in his usual smooth, oily way. His fat face wore a subtle look, half-flattering, half-threatening. "We have remarked, Princess, that you are no longer a child. Nor are you the bookish girl who had such an odd liking for the company of scholars. You will soon be fifteen—almost a woman. Today you have displayed the woman's natural instinct for beautiful and costly objects and the woman's natural desire to be admired and envied. That is admirable. It is proper. Leave books and weighty subjects to others. Occupy the pedestal and be worshiped. Too much thinking only brings wrinkles to a woman's face. Leave the thinking to others."

"What others?" She watched him closely.

"To myself, for one. To General Achillas, for another. Let us be your friends. Let us guide you, plan for you, scheme for you, and when you are queen of Egypt we will take from your shoulders all that is annoying and worrisome to you. You must be free to amuse yourself."

He would have patted her hand with his thick, sausage-like fingers but she drew back. "What do you say, General Achillas?"

"I am a blunt soldier." His proud and haughty face made him a strange man to consort with one like Pothinus, yet the two were often together. "I command the army and the navy. Between the cleverness of Pothinus, who knows how to plan political strategy, and my power as general, your position as queen will be safe. We will guarantee it. You will be able to deck yourself with all the jewels you want and amuse yourself as you please. We will take care of the rest."

She was so furious she could not sit still, and got up and stood in front of them. "The price of my safety and my pleasures being that I become a puppet in your hands. I am to do your bidding. Is it not enough that you have my brother under your control, Pothinus? Must I, too, yield my will to yours? You will protect me, General Achillas, with your army—how dare you speak of it as yours! The army of Egypt is sworn to defend and obey the Ptolemies. Must I kneel to you for that defense? When I am queen I will rule, not you. Get out of my rooms!"

Achillas' face was purple-dark with anger. Pothinus had lost his smirk. There was poisonous hatred in the look he gave her as he left. "You will regret this, I warn you," he said, softly.

She had made two very powerful enemies. After they had gone she threw a cushion to the floor, seized a vase and smashed it in her anger. She paid no attention to the dozens of slaves who were straightening up her apartment after the guests had disarranged it, carrying out amphoras of wine and fruit juices and platters of half-eaten food. She realized that she had won one victory, in pleasing her father, and now she faced other and worse problems.

It had not been wise to anger those two men. Could she have helped it? Could she have smiled at them, knowing they meant to have her under their thumbs? At the thought of it, suddenly her own anger cooled, and she threw herself on a couch to think soberly.

She was too intelligent to let herself be managed by others. She was too proud to be flattered into complaisance, too self-willed to be guided in anything except small matters. Yet she would need friends. She would need advisers who would not try to control her. Where would she find them?

During the next two years she grew to understand a little but to be perplexed by much. Her father continued, in his careless way, to be pleased by her. Though he paid slight attention to any of his children, she was his favorite.

Yet she sensed that Auletes' power was hollow. Decisions were made in the council room without him. More and more she saw that Pothinus and Achillas were gathering about them a party of Alexandrians who would be devoted to her brother, as Ganymede and his group were devoted to Arsinoë.

Her own friends were not politicians. She made the mistake of not cultivating politicians; they bored her. She preferred the wise philosophy of Olympus or the exciting discoveries of Sosigenes or the light and amusing companionship of Appolodorus.

Saat tried to warn her. "Now is the time, Princess, when you should be carefully selecting those men who will make a strong party around you."

She was too young and too inexperienced to know how to go about it. She was too proud to let others do it for her. So those years drifted on. She changed, physically. She was no longer so thin. Her face developed a striking quality which some called beauty and others thought merely odd. Her eyes were large. Her nose was aquiline, but not the high, thin-boned type so much admired. Her chin had a suggestion of blunt strength which was offset by a mouth intensely feminine. Her two best features were her eyes, which changed expression with every mood, and her voice.

Young men were beginning to notice and court her.

Though she was growing up, physically, she was not maturing in wisdom. Time hung idly on her hands. She gave parties. She hoped in this way to make friends for herself, but she did not know how to flatter this man or listen to another or take sides with one against another, nor did she fathom all of the feuds and alliances that made up the strong and weak elements in the aristocracy. So did time pass.

Suddenly, in the year 52 B.C., Auletes, Ptolemy XI, died.

The ceremonies of funeral for the King and the coronation of both brother and sister were solemn and religious. At seventeen, she took precedence over her ten-year-old brother, who was now Ptolemy XII, and she went alone to the temple with the Egyptian high priest and made offerings so that the Ka, the spirit, of her father would not die but would continue to live. She was carried through the streets on a golden litter for everyone to see, and she was hailed in extravagant terms as the "Come-Back-to-Life of Isis"—"Chosen of Ptah"—"Child of the Sun."

She and her brother ascended the twin thrones and each had the double crown of Upper and Lower Egypt placed on their heads.

She took it for granted that she would rule. Her brother was only ten, still a child. He would be a king in name only until he came of age.

One week after she was crowned Queen Cleopatra, the period of deep mourning was considered finished. The pleasure-loving Alexandrians demanded a celebration, so a chariot race in the stadium was arranged. It was their favorite sport. Cleopatra must be present to award the prize to the winner.

Olympus sat next to her. "You look the same as when you were just a princess," he said to her, smiling. "Do you feel like a queen?"

"I'm trying to, but it doesn't seem real yet. I want so much to be a strong queen. I will never have people laugh at me as they laughed at my father," she said.

Olympus took no part in politics but he was a keen observer. "You will need to be strong and I think you will be. You resemble your earlier ancestors, the strong Ptolemies. Will you model yourself after them?"

"Yes, and after Alexander the Great. It seems to me, Olympus, that the most important thing is not ever to be afraid."

He pulled at his lip. "As a doctor, I can only advise you that a little bit of fear can be a good thing; it can make you cautious so that you do not run head first into danger."

The great race-course stadium was filled now with spectators who were wild with excitement over the promise of the day's sport. They were yelling for the races to start.

Olympus began to speak but he was interrupted. It was General Achillas.

"Queen Cleopatra." He bowed, a very short bow that was more mockery than sincere. "May I claim the privilege of this bench beside your chair?" A physician had not the stature of a general, and he must politely give way.

She could only say yes. Her brother, on the other side of her, was leaning forward, restlessly eager for the races, talking with animation to Pothinus. Cleopatra felt herself hemmed in by these three, with no friend near her.

The first race started. The stands were full of screaming, delirious people, shouting encouragement.

If appearances counted for anything, she was every inch a queen; dignified when others around her behaved as if they were mad. She was trying hard. Let no one say she acted the clown, as they had said of Auletes!

Four more races went by; then came the major race of the day. Six of the finest chariots and drivers were entered. The stadium rocked with shouts and cheers. One chariot turned over. Horses and driver were badly hurt. Another lost a wheel on the third round. Then the winner came in.

As the hoarse cheers died down, the winner climbed out of his chariot and strode over to a position in front of the royal box. He held his head down, modestly, waiting for the laurel wreath to be put on it.

Cleopatra stretched out her hand for the wreath, but she was too late. As if by accident, Achillas had his hand on her arm, and was pulling at it saying at the same time, "See how handsome he is, Queen Cleopatra. Does he not touch your heart—forgive me, did I interfere with you?"

She jerked her hand loose and reached for the laurel wreath.

It was gone. Pothinus had picked it up and placed it in her brother's hands. So it was Ptolemy XII, not Cleopatra, who rose to his feet to be applauded by everyone and be the center of all eyes as he advanced and placed the wreath on the winner's head.

"You did that on purpose, Achillas!" Gone was her dignity. She was spitting like a cat.

"Did what? Have I offended you?" He was smiling.

Now she knew that Olympus had been right. She would have been wise to fear these two men. She was in danger. They were going to do their best to take the power away from her and use it to their best advantage through the boy-king. The clever trick they had worked just now was a sign of what she could expect.

She was dazed. The crown on her head felt heavy.

Here William Shakespeare pictures the more mature Cleopatra as she sailed down the Nile to meet Mark Antony.

CLEOPATRA'S BARGE

by WILLIAM SHAKESPEARE

The barge she sat in, like a burnish'd throne
Burn'd on the water: the poop was beaten gold;
Purple the sails, and so perfumed, that
The winds were lovesick with them: the oars were silver;
Which to the tune of flutes kept stroke, and made
The water, which they beat, to follow faster,
As amorous of their strokes. For her own person,
It beggar'd all description: she did lie

ANTONY AND CLEOPATRA, Act II, Scene 2.

In her pavilion, (cloth of gold, of tissue,)
O'er-picturing that Venus, where we see,
The fancy outwork nature; on each side her,
Stood pretty dimpled boys, like smiling Cupids,
With diverse-color'd fans, whose wind did seem
To glow the delicate cheeks which they did cool,
And what they undid, did.

Her gentlewomen, like the Nereides,
So many mermaids, tended her i' the eyes,
And made their bends adornings: at the helm
A seeming Mermaid steers; the silken tackle
Swell with the touches of those flower-soft hands,
That rarely frame the office. From the barge
A strange invisible perfume hits the sense
Of the adjacent wharfs. The city cast
Her people out upon her; and Antony,
Enthron'd in the marketplace, did sit alone,
Whistling to the air: which, but for vacancy,
Had gone to gaze on Cleopatra too,
And made a gap in nature . . .
Age cannot wither her, nor custom stale
Her infinite variety . . .

NORA LOFTS

Eleanor of Aquitaine

Eleanor was a beautiful princess who became the richest marriage prize in Europe in the power struggle between France and England in the twelfth century. A woman of destiny, she married two kings—a Capet and then a Plantagenet. She had two sons who succeeded to the English throne. One king was strong; that was Richard the Lion-Hearted. One king was weak; he was called John Lackland.

IT WAS SPRING AGAIN in Aquitaine. In the orchards outside the city of Poitiers the plum and peach and pear blossoms had lost their first brightness and the petals were falling, but the tide of gay wild flowers had run over the orchard grass and over the roadside verges and all the air was full of the sweetness of newly cut hay. The fragrance reached even the high room where Eleanor sat before her looking glass while Amaria brushed her long hair.

From ELEANOR THE QUEEN, by Nora Lofts.

Fifteen years since she had seen the spring in her own land! She would be perfectly happy if only the children were here with her. She missed them more than she had expected; for in Paris, owing to all the regulations which governed their upbringing, she had actually spent little time with them. Still, they were there and she was always devising little games for them or thinking of amusing things to tell them, so that her visits, though brief, should be gay and have meaning.

She sighed, then said, "Today, Amaria, we'll take a holiday. For ten whole days I have worked at affairs of state, asking and answering dull questions, and going through those dismal accounts. Today I shall leave it all; we'll ride out and watch the haymaking, and take some food and eat it under a tree, then sleep a little and ride back in the cool of the evening. I must admit, Amaria, I find it very delightful to say, 'I will do this, or that,' and not have to ask permission beforehand, or listen to reproaches afterwards."

She could see, in the looking glass, the glumness of Amaria's face.

"What ails you?" she asked, as Amaria stayed silent. "If your head aches, you need not come."

"If you ride, I shall ride. But I think you would do well to stay within the city walls at least, though even there, God knows, you may not be safe. It looks to me as though we may never be safe again."

"Oh come! You make much out of nothing. Two little scuffles on our way down from Paris! Just silly boys' pranks. And we were well protected."

"I lack your stout heart. I can see that when men protect women from other men, some of the blows they aim at one another may fall on the women they are protecting."

"No blow came near enough to us to disarrange our headgear. What has happened, Amaria? You were not so timid when we rode on crusade," Eleanor protested.

"I was always timid. At least, on crusade, we knew our enemies —their clothes and their faces betrayed them. Those boys, as you call them, who lay in wait for you the other day at the ford looked like Christians and we were nearly taken unaware. There are two young noblemen who have tried to take you—run off and marry you—already . . . and greedy, ambitious young noblemen are common as dandelions. Yet there you are, talking of lying down in the sun to sleep! I do beg you, my lady, if we ride out today, to order a strong escort."

"If it comforts you, I will do so. But remember, we are now in my own domain."

"And do the Aquitainian nobles lack ambition or greed?"

"Ah, but I am no longer an innocent young girl, Amaria. Once the thought of being run off with and married against my will did frighten me. The man who tried it now would find that he had caught more than he bargained for. That I do assure you."

"Boldness," said Amaria with a sourness unusual to her, "is mainly the capacity for underrating danger. With a gag in your mouth and your hands tied behind you—which is how the Lady Beatrix was led to the altar not ten years ago—you'd be as helpless as the next woman." She dropped the tress of hair she was holding and passed the brush up and down the palm of her hand. "What I'm going to say may be distasteful, but there's nothing for it but for you to marry again—and as soon as possible."

"And whom do you propose I should marry? You seem to have planned it all, Amaria. Boldness in planning, allow me to say, is mainly the capacity to underrate difficulties."

Amaria, for the first time that morning, smiled.

"I know the man, my lady. And so, I think, must you."

"Well, name him!" She looked into the mirror and her clear green eyes met Amaria's gray ones in the shadowy depths.

"Henry Plantagenet, Duke of Normandy," Amaria said, and saw the white lids blink, saw the faintest possible color creep up from Eleanor's throat to lose itself in the pale clear rose of her cheeks. Then, no more than half a second too late, she laughed.

"Amaria, unless that young man has added another birthday to his tally, he is eighteen years old!"

"What of it? The last fifteen years have gone lightly over you, my lady. We were saying the other day that you look no older now than when you left Aquitaine; and the young Duke is a man, whatever his years. More a man, if you ask me, than his father. Surely you must have marked, when they both came to the French court, how he always took the lead, how sometimes in their talk his father would look to him before giving an answer, instead of the other way about. You must have noticed."

"The thing I marked most about him was a strange resemblance to someone I knew many years ago . . . someone of whom I was very fond . . ." She brooded for a moment, remembering that first innocent love. Then she roused herself and said, "Go on with the brushing, Amaria, or we shall miss the best of the day."

"You'd do well to think over what I have said," Amaria persisted. "Married to him, you'd be safe. And he admired you, I could see that."

"Even so, marriage between us is well-nigh impossible. If the thought entered his head—which I doubt it ever would—he would dismiss it; the King of France would object strongly; after all, these Plantagenets hold Brittany and Anjou from the French crown, great and powerful though they may be."

"Ah well, I didn't mean tomorrow or the next day. By all accounts, the young Duke will be King of England one day, or know the reason why, and then he'll be independent of the King of France. Bear him in mind, my lady; and, in the meantime, take no risks of being married by force." She glanced toward the window. "There'll be no riding abroad today, anyway; a storm is blowing up."

"Don't sound so *pleased*," said Eleanor.

The room grew darker as Amaria looped and coiled the long hair and fixed it with the silver and ivory pins. When it was done, Eleanor went and stood by the window. The black-purple cloud had covered the sun's face, but from its lower edge one ray of concentrated light escaped to fall upon the castle courtyard, the bridge that linked it to the town, and the huddled roofs of the nearest houses. It all looked unreal, a scene from a nightmare.

As she stared, a little knot of horsemen clattered up to the far side of the bridge. One man detached himself to ride on alone and halt for a moment on the bridge, raking the castle with an arrogant appraising stare.

Her breath stopped as she recognized the solid, barrel-chested,

long-legged figure, the cocksure set of the head, the red hair showing under the cap with its jaunty sprig of broom—the *planta
genista*, from which his family took its name. She had just said
that he would hardly dare to come, and here he was, looking just
as he had looked when he came, arrogantly and belatedly, to pay
his allegiance to Louis, his overlord—so young, so handsome, so
high-hearted. Her eyes had followed him then, and she had
thought, Naturally he attracts me; he is the son I should have
had. Then, hearing his voice saying brief, downright things, she
was reminded of Richard de Vaux and imagined that *there* lay
the secret of his attraction for her.

Now, looking down from her high window, she knew that
neither of these reasons was the true one.

Suddenly breathless, she turned from the window and said,
"Amaria, quick! My best gown. He has come!"

"The Plantagenet? Well, well. They say, 'Talk of the Devil,'
do they not?" She hurried toward the great press where the few
gowns which Eleanor had brought with her from Paris lay folded,
and sprinkled with lavender and rosemary. As she lifted the lid,
the lightning struck into the room like a sword and, immediately
after, the thunder sounded as though a thousand battering rams
were assaulting the gates of Heaven. White-lipped, Amaria
gasped, "He comes with the storm. Oh, what an omen, my lady!
What an omen!"

Eleanor swooped across the room, took up a gown, and began
to shake it from its folds.

"Don't stand there like an image, Amaria, run out and tell
them—De Rancon and the rest—to receive him formally, *formally*; to take him to wait in the anteroom, and offer refreshment. Send Sybille to me, and then run on and tell all my
women—their finest clothes—and quickly, quickly."

Henry Plantagenet, Duke of Normandy, acknowledged heir to
Anjou, and, in the eyes of many, rightful heir to England, prided
himself upon being "a plain, blunt man." Reared in the saddle,
the hunting field, and the stern school of war, he had no time
and less liking for what he called "nonsense and mummery." In

his own court he was as accessible as a farmer or shopkeeper; a man stated his business, was granted an audience, told to say what was to be said as briefly as possible, and dismissed. Today he himself was the one who came asking an audience, and, when he had dismounted and said in his loud firm voice that he wished to speak privately to the Duchess of Aquitaine, he expected to be led straight into her presence and left alone to say his say.

But in the small anteroom, kept waiting, surrounded by the few nobles and knights whom Eleanor had gathered around her in the ten days since her homecoming, he began to feel uncomfortable. These Aquitainians, gay and careless as they could be at times, had a talent for formality and ceremony. He remembered that in the old Duke's time this court had been the cradle of the most elegant form of chivalry. There had actually been a kind of school, called the Court of Love, at which young knights were taught how to behave toward ladies; how to please them by turning pretty speeches, by making music, by singing songs. It was all elaborate, set to pattern, a kind of play acting; in fact, hitherto Henry had dismissed it all as the greatest nonsense and a wicked waste of time. Now he wondered . . . and as he stood, impatiently slapping his leg with his gloves, he gained less pleasure than usual from his thought—"I'm only a plain, blunt man."

When at last he was confronted by Eleanor, wearing all her finery, surrounded by the gaily decked ladies who had been hastily mustered to form as impressive a court as possible, he was annoyed to find himself nervous; and, to the first remarks addressed to him, he gave answers so short and awkward that even in his own ears they sounded unmannerly.

Soon he rallied; he was a plain, blunt man; he had no time to waste; he had something to say which he did not intend to say before this gathering of smiling posturing popinjays, so presently he said, "Your Highness, I have that to say which is for your ear alone. Can we—or they—withdraw?"

The words rapped out so harshly that Eleanor knew a moment's doubt; perhaps, after all, he had come on some political errand; perhaps he was meditating making war on his overlord, the King of France, and saw in her, the divorced Queen of France, a likely ally. Well, if he wished to be businesslike, she would match his manner. She stood up, abandoning the advantage of the high-backed chair in which she had seated herself for effect, and said, "Come with me, my lord."

When they were alone, he refused the seat she offered him. "I always stand, save when I ride or sleep," he said. Standing stiffly before her, he went on, "It must be clear to you why I am here. A year ago when you were Queen of France and there seemed little likelihood that the divorce would ever be granted, I wished with all my heart you were a free woman. Now you are, and I . . . Madam, I am a plain, blunt man, no hand at pretty speeches, and a sorry figure I'd cut at these courts of love you think so highly of in Aquitaine . . . so I can only offer you my hand and have done with it."

He stared at her with his light, bright, over-prominent eyes, and she could see that he expected her to reply to this proposal in a manner equally brisk. Some of the assurance went out of him when she smiled and said nothing.

He waited; then, with considerably less jauntiness, he went on. "At the moment I can offer you nothing that you haven't yourself, already. Aquitaine is wider than Normandy, wider than Normandy and Anjou; and, if what I have seen during a hard ride is a fair sample, it is richer and more productive. But with God's help—and yours, my lady, if you care to give it—I shall have England, too, before long. And the crown of England will become you better than the crown of France ever did. What's comical in that? Why are you laughing?" The ringing merry laughter, so seldom heard of late, broke irrepressibly from her.

"Not—I assure you—at you, my lord Duke. No, I am laughing at all the minstrels and poets with their tales of love. I am told that I am not ill-favored, and I have traveled farther than most women. I have now received three proposals and not a word of love in any one of them. My lord of France said to me, "Madam, a marriage has been arranged between us; I trust you do not find me distasteful." That was forgivable in him, for he was reared to be a monk and monks are not trained to make proposals. Then there was an emir in Antioch who addressed me through my uncle, who knew his language; *he* said literally, "If you will leave your husband, I will dispose of my eldest wife and you shall rule the others." There was excuse for him; he was a Saracen. But for you, my lord, I find it hard to find excuse, just as I find it hard to decide whether you really want my hand in marriage—or my help in your bid for the English throne."

She spoke laughingly, teasingly, but no spark of answering amusement lighted Henry's face. He drew away angrily. "By God's head, madam, I thought better of you! A year ago, in the court of France, there was a moment in the talk—you had been sitting there looking as pretty and innocent as a flower—and then you spoke and cut through all the flummery and the nonsense like a sickle through wheat, going straight to the heart of the matter. And I was astonished. A woman in ten thousand, I thought to myself, and to Louis I could scarcely speak civilly on account of the envy that was in me. The moment you are free and it is decent for me to speak, haven't I followed you here? . . . so close that I rode in your dust almost . . . though I know that the moment Louis hears of it he'll call me a faithless vassal and most likely will attack my province."

Henry swung about and began walking to and fro, as was his habit in moments of agitation. In a calmer voice he went on, "I said, 'with God's help, and yours,' but never think I *need* help from you or anyone. It is true that with Aquitaine behind me I should be more formidable, but if all Europe sank into the depths of the sea, leaving me afloat in my nightshirt, I still would have England—or die in the attempt. It is my right; and, if the usurper who drove my mother out and is driving the country to beggary by his mismanagement will not acknowledge my claim, I'll force it from him. When I said, 'with your help,' I meant that when the crown of England was set on your head you could feel it was yours by right—not yours because some creeping politician had arranged it, or because you're fair of face. By the rood, I was fool enough to think that point of view would find favor with you!"

His weatherbeaten face had darkened, the light eyes were even more prominent; they stared at her defiantly. After a moment's silence Eleanor said in a surprisingly humble voice: "Truth to tell, it does. And I have no doubt that with, or without, backing from me you will have your England. I remember your visit to Paris . . . I remember thinking . . ." (For all his dislike of soft speeches, Henry listened eagerly) ". . . thinking that I pitied Stephen of England having you for an enemy."

For the first time Henry smiled. "In Normandy, my lady, we have the saying, 'Good enemy, good lover.' All I ask of you is the chance to prove that I can be one as well as the other."

"Now that," Eleanor said, "is quite a pretty speech."

"It was not so intended," Henry said; but, as though encouraged, he added, "I will tell you another thing. I am no monk. A sweet smile, a pretty face, even a stray curl, can bring me down as a falcon brings down a hawk, but since the day when I saw you in Paris I have given no thought to any woman. There's a yellow-headed Hohenstaufen girl—and if you think your lands and men will help forward my ambition, think what such a bond with the Holy Roman Empire could do for me. I was on the verge of making an offer for her hand, but, once I'd seen you, she looked as tasteless as a plate of cold porridge—without salt." He seemed to become aware of the fact that he was indulging in the despised pastime of bandying words. "Well, all's been said now. Will you take me or not?"

"It is no decision to make in a moment." Eleanor was grave now. "After all, this will affect all my life—and all yours. And, to be honest with you, the advantage is by no means all on your side. As someone who has my good at heart pointed out only this morning, I must either marry again or go about with an armed bodyguard all my days; a woman alone, a woman of property, seems to be regarded by most men as a plum for picking; and so she shall be while priests can be found to perform the marriage ceremony whether the woman concerned be willing or not."

"Ah!" said Henry; quite unwittingly she had invited him to mount his hobbyhorse. "There you put your finger on it. The Church is wise; no matter what problem arises, the Church has the right, wise answer. The Church foresaw, centuries ago, some poor woman being carried off and married against her will; so it decreed that the priest should ask in a loud audible voice, 'Wilt thou take this man?' and that the woman should say—and be heard by the whole congregation—'I do.' Or, provided she had cause, 'No, I do not.' Holy Mother Church was on guard against the greedy and the unscrupulous. But the *priests* . . . ah, there is the weakness. Sheltered and pampered, they think themselves above the law; they break it with impunity; they defy God, and man . . ." He broke off and swallowed. "Dear lady, this is not the moment . . . but you will find when you know me better that two bees buzz in my bonnet. One is my right to be King of England; the other is that priests should stand level with other men in the sight of the law. Until they do, the whole thing is a mockery. Why, not long since, a woman of some substance, a widow to boot, and sixty years old, was dragged to the altar, gagged and bound, and married to a man who coveted her property. Now that could never happen in Normandy."

"Why not?"

"My priests know my mind. There are loopholes that I have not yet closed—places where canon law and secular law do not fit side by side, but where I rule at least, they are mindful to obey the canon law because it is their bulwark against the other."

Eleanor's heart warmed to him.

He blundered on. "I'm a good churchman, but I'm a soldier, too, and I hold that a priest who breaks the law of the Church, or the law of the land in which he lives, is as guilty as a soldier who deserts to the other side or goes to sleep on guard. Some rogue the other day—he'd come from Venice with some stuff to sell—was telling me about a country where cows were holy. Can you imagine that? They can do no wrong; if they break into your garden and eat all your lettuces, or into your field and trample down your growing corn, you have no redress. It's a poor heathen country, of course, but it seems to me if we're going to let priests disregard all law, they'll end as holy cows. I'm talking too much, wasting time which you need for thinking things over and making up your mind."

But Eleanor already knew what her answer was to be.

GRACE HUMPHREY

Catherine of Aragon, The Princess Who Married Two Brothers

The royal children of Ferdinand and Isabella, rulers of Aragon and Castile, grew up in a fairyland setting. They lived in the magnificent palace of the Moorish kings, the gorgeous and romantic Alhambra.

The Infanta Catherine was taught to speak and write Latin, Spanish, Italian, and Flemish. But she never learned English, although she was destined to marry two English princes and to spend most of her life in England.

From THE STORY OF THE CATHERINES, by Grace Humphrey.

"WHAT! The English asked for a million crowns for the Infanta's dowry?"

The Queen of Castile leaned forward and gazed sharply at her ambassador who was reporting the result of his journey to London.

"Yes, your Majesty, a million crowns. I scowled. I held up my hands. I hinted something about life's uncertainty in England and then asked plainly how their last four rulers had met their deaths. We debated and argued. At last we settled on two hundred thousand crowns as your youngest daughter's marriage portion."

"Then it is all arranged?"

"All but one detail. The King's minister insists he must see the Infanta Catherine. I myself saw Prince Arthur—and more than once. I saw him gorgeously dressed, then stripped that I might be sure his body was well formed and his skin fair, then peacefully sleeping."

"And what is your opinion of the Prince of Wales?"

"A pretty baby—he's twenty months old—yet very delicate. But fair—fair; after the dark Moors his fairness seems wonderful."

"But I will not," declared Queen Isabella firmly, "I will not invite this minister here to inspect my little daughter. I have not forgotten the ordeal I went through when an English earl came to see if I would do as a bride for their Edward IV—and then he married somebody else in spite of his council. Submit Catherine to such a trial? Never!"

"But the matter has gone so far. Would you be willing perhaps to let the King's commissioner see her when the Infanta would know nothing about it?"

"Well, arrange for that."

So the Englishman was invited to a bullfight in the nursery-palace. The Queen was there with her children. She held up Catherine and the child's pleasant appearance satisfied him.

The treaty was signed: the Infanta, three years old, to wed the Prince of Wales, a few months more than two. As early as she could remember, Catherine grew up with the knowledge that some day she was to marry the son and heir of the King of England.

Spain and England both feared that the other country might break this agreement, and three times the children were betrothed by proxy. At last Henry VII demanded that Catherine come at once to London. This was the high tide of Spanish prosperity: the Moors were expelled, the voyages of Columbus were giving the land prestige and wealth. Nothing was spared to make the suite of this princess splendid—three bishops, a count and countess, her duenna, ladies of honor, and four young girls as her attendants; to say nothing of retainers and servants, and jewels valued at twenty thousand crowns. Thus the bride of fifteen, a striking girl with rich auburn hair, set sail for a foreign shore and a husband she had never seen.

At two cities on the coast the English prepared a welcome for the Infanta, but a hurricane drove the Spanish ships into Plymouth harbor. The good folk there made haste to hang out their flags, crowded to the shore and cheered lustily for Catherine of Aragon.

The Infanta continued her journey, met at every town with brave display and speeches of welcome. The last stop showed the most brilliant gathering of all—four hundred knights and gentlemen in scarlet and black; and at their head a sturdy, fair-haired boy of ten, Arthur's younger brother Henry.

To the delight of the Londoners, when Catherine made her formal entrance into the city she wore the picturesque dress of her native land.

"See, she's riding on a mule! Is that the fashion in Spain?"

"Look at her large round hat, shaped like a cardinal's, and tied on with a lace of gold. All her ladies have the same kind."

"Isn't her long hair lovely! It streams over her shoulders and floats in the wind. How pretty her carnation-colored veil is against it!"

"What a high forehead! Extraordinarily high—why, it takes half her face!"

"With her blue eyes and light complexion she doesn't seem very Spanish. You know, they say she has English blood—descended from John of Gaunt—so she herself has some claim to the throne. She's not a foreigner, but a princess returning to her own land."

"Who is the tall lad riding beside her? A striking pair they are."

"Why, it's the King's second son, Henry, Duke of York. Big for his age, isn't he? As vigorous and sturdy as the Prince of Wales is delicate."

Two days later at the splendid wedding in St. Paul's this same boy, dressed in white velvet and gold, proudly led in the bride. She wore over her head a Spanish mantilla of white silk, and half hid her face with a scarf bordered with gold and pearls and precious stones. Her white satin gown, as the herald's description has come down to us, was very large, with many plaits in sleeves and skirt; and below the waist round hoops that bore out the dress from her body after her country's manner—the first far-thingale in England.

The bridegroom, arrayed in white satin, joined her and they were married by the Archbishop of Canterbury and his nineteen assisting bishops and abbots. There followed the wedding din-ner, a tournament at Westminster Hall, masquing and banquets, elaborate pageants and dancing—days of feasting and festivity.

Shortly before Christmas the young married people set out from London and rode leisurely across England to Ludlow Castle on the Welsh border. They had a little court there, but Cath-erine could not have been very happy. She could talk with her husband only in Latin. He was very frail and all too soon really ill. Early in April he died—either of a plague or of a wasting disease.

With weeping and sore lamentation he was buried in the ca-thedral at Worcester. His tomb is there today in the chancel, en-shrined within the walls of a beautiful little chapel, adorned with carvings and many statuettes. One of the figures is Catherine's, wearing the coronet of the Princess of Wales and holding in her hand a castle, the emblem of Castile.

The marriage which had taken so many years of negotiating was suddenly ended in less than six months. What was to be done with the Spanish princess, at sixteen left a widow in a strange land? On the very day the news of Arthur's death reached them, before they wrote a letter of condolence, Ferdinand and Isabella sent off an emissary to England to make arrangements for bringing their daughter home, but with secret orders to suggest that she marry the King's second son, now heir to the throne.

Only half her dowry had been paid. The miserly Henry VII was eager to get the balance, not surrender the sums already in his hands. Moreover it was highly important to keep Spain's friendship and so strengthen his position against France. Never mind if Catherine was five years older than the young prince. They were betrothed by proxy.

"Hold!" exclaimed some people in England and some in Spain. "He is her brother-in-law. Is it lawful for him to wed the widow of his brother Arthur? Doesn't this close relationship bring their marriage within the class forbidden by the church?"

The rulers of Spain sent to the Pope for a dispensation and this was granted. The special permission from God's representative on earth stopped all the murmurs of disapproval. But it was understood that the twelve-year-old Prince of Wales was to grow up before the marriage took place.

And while the difference in their ages seemed less and less as time went on, poor Catherine's seven years of widowhood were difficult and unhappy. Henry VII promised to provide for her household, but did not. By law she was entitled to a third of Arthur's income, but she received nothing. Thus her father-in-law hoped to force her father to hurry the last installment of her dowry.

Between the two she was helpless. She could not pay her servants and her ladies-in-waiting. She had to go into debt for the one new gown she had—a black velvet mourning dress. She ran up bills, not for luxuries, but for food. Over and over she wrote pitiful letters to Ferdinand, pleading that he pay the rest of her dowry so that she would not be dependent on the King of England.

Was she happy at court? She had no close friends, save her Spanish suite. She spoke English with difficulty. She was not well. After the warmth and sunshine of Granada it took her years to get used to the English climate, so cool and damp. She had heavy colds and coughs. Again and again she had attacks of ague that she could not shake off.

Henry VII postponed the marriage more than once. But when he lay dying in the spring of 1509 he summoned his son.

"The world and all its deceits are fading away. I entreat you to wed Catherine of Aragon. It is my express command."

Long afterward men recalled this and argued, "At such a moment would the King have said so if the marriage involved a crime?"

For seven years the pros and cons of this question had been discussed by the council.

Henry cut short any further discussion by marrying Catherine of Aragon in the palace at Greenwich, and the service was performed by that very archbishop who had argued against this step. It would have been easy, no doubt, for the King to have released himself from an engagement made for him when he was still a boy. But they loved each other.

"If we were still free," wrote Henry to King Ferdinand, "her would we yet choose for our wife before all other."

As striking a picture as before the two made when twelve days later they went to London for their coronation. The bride of twenty-three rode in a litter of white and gold, borne by two white palfreys. She wore a robe of white embroidered satin. Her long hair was hanging down. Her ladies were richly attired in cloth of silver.

The bridegroom, eighteen in a few days, rode a great courser. His dress was crimson velvet edged with ermine, over a coat of gold, with a stomacher that blazed with rubies and emeralds and diamonds and pearls. His attendants were nine children of honor, all in blue velvet powdered with golden fleur-de-lys, representing the nine kingdoms and provinces of which he claimed to be head.

"In all Europe Henry VIII is the finest prize in the matrimonial market," men declared. "Every one sings his praises. He speaks four or five languages. He plays almost every instrument, and sings and composes. He is very tall and strong and delights in sports. No wonder he's so popular with all classes. Aye, he's a fine, upstanding youth, handsome and accomplished!"

One of Henry's gifts to his wife was the missal which had belonged to his mother. In the book he wrote in French:

"If your remembrance is as great as my affection, I shall not be forgotten in your daily prayers, for I am yours forever,
HENRY R."

ELSWYTH THANE

Elizabeth I of England

Queen Elizabeth I of England (1533–1603) rivals Cleopatra in popularity with historians, novelists, and poets. Like Cleopatra, she could fascinate men and did not hesitate to use her charms for her own ends. But since her first love was for England, she emerges as a capable queen rather than as a romantic woman.

The novelist Elswyth Thane gives us a portrait of Elizabeth Tudor in those dangerous, important years while she was growing up and preparing to be a queen.

SHE SMOOTHED the pale blue silk of her dress with anxious fingertips, pressing firmly with her thumb where a small loop of gilt braid hung loose. She was to have had a new dress weeks ago, but the King had forgotten again, and this one had been let down and faced back with a strip cut from an old blue petticoat of Mary's.

From THE TUDOR WENCH, by Elswyth Thane.

She frowned down at herself, less in bad temper than in anxiety, for she wished to look her best today and she loved pretty clothes always. Ah, well, perhaps he would not notice that the blue silk was shabby, he was probably quite old and no doubt he did not see as well as he might. Everyone at Court was old, except Edward, who was too young to notice things. Whereas Elizabeth Tudor was six.

An hour after midday a farm lad had come panting across the fields, goggle-eyed with news—gentlemen on horseback were approaching from London where the King was. Hertford Castle slipped promptly into panic. Mary flew off to change her dress. Fires were built and rushes freshened. The kitchen bustled with the preparation of meats and tarts and jellies, so that soon an odor of cloves and cooking stole up the stairs. Someone fell upon Elizabeth, who sat murmuring her Latin verbs into an exercise book, and washed her face and hands—there were little tendrils round her ears still damp from the cloth—and bundled her into her best dress, the blue silk with gilt braid.

The gilt braid showed tarnished beside the juvenile brightness of the cheerful reddish ringlets at the edge of her cap. The cap was new and clean, anyway. She herself had helped to sew it.

The sunbeam where she stood was perceptibly warmer than the rest of the high room, with its myriad panes of glass in a bow casement, round which the hangings stirred in a perpetual draught. She paused there in the sun, spreading her hands to it as to a fire. Their natural delicacy was chapped and red with cold, but they were very clean today, with the nails freshly trimmed. She saw them now for the first time, really—those hands which were always to be her greatest beauty; noticed that the trimming of nails was enhancing and approved; wondered, greatly daring, if Mary would allow one to use a bit of the rosewater lately sent her as a gift by Lady Hertford, along with the quince pies which were all gone days ago. Mary's hands were knobby at the knuckles, but Mary had rings and Mary had a wonderful gold chain which had come from Spain with Catherine of Aragon all those years ago when she was a young bride, younger than Mary was now. Apparently one's own mother, also dead, had bequeathed one no trinkets . . . ? Elizabeth Tudor was leaving babyhood behind.

A door opened in the end of the room and a new draught came in, raising the warm ashes on the great hearth below its carved and burnished oak overmantel. She shivered in the sun and turned, expecting the awaited summons. But it was only a lad with a log to mend the fire.

He grinned frankly at the little lonely figure in the center of the room and went about his business with the fire, his blue eyes atwinkle at her smallness and her dignity.

The room filled slowly with a murk of smoke.

"It wants the bellows, Dickon," she remarked at last, and coughed.

"It do, your Grace," he agreed, pleased again at how she always remembered his name and called him by it; (unlike the Lady Mary with her gruff-voiced *"Boy!"*) "I'll blow."

He blew, and smoke eddied out into the room. The bellows were downstairs in the great hall, which was in readiness for the visitors—a long way, through cold stone corridors. He blew till he was purple and a glint of flame shot up.

Her Grace drew near, watching.

" 'Tis a good pair of lungs, Dickon!" She laughed, and eyed his apoplectic color with approval.

"Oh, ay," he boasted, swelling. "No need for bellows, my Lady!"

Her Grace came nearer.

"It was left too long," she observed sagely.

"I've been at the fire in the hall," he explained between great puffs. "We've had a time down there, I can tell you! There's nobody gets off without a clout on the ear today!"

Small shoes with blue bows toed the hearth.

"Blow there," she directed, pointing. "Just there at the side— it's brightest." And stooping, she added her tiny breath to his. "Blow, Dickon—blow!" she cried, pink-faced and laughing. "Together, now—I'm helping—*blow!*"

"Elizabeth!"

The tornado ceased on a splutter and Lady Bryan, the governess, bore down upon them. Dickon ducked, but her expert hand

landed sharply on the side of his head as he dived for the door
which had just swung to behind her. Elizabeth, always valiant
in a crisis, snatched his cap from the hearth and hurled it well
and truly past him, so that he caught it up, Atalanta-like, in flight.
The great door banged on his escape.

Her Grace drew a decorous sigh and smoothed back her ruddy
curls, unconscious of a smudge across her cheek.

"The fire was left too long," she remarked in masterly imita-
tion of Mary's most royal manner. "I have been cold."

But Lady Bryan would not play that game today. She fell to
tweaking here and brushing there, and she scrubbed the smudged
cheek with a corner of her kerchief till the thin skin burned,
scolding all the while—could not my Lady Elizabeth be trusted
out of her women's sight but she must roll in the ashes—was it
not enough that they had the King's messenger unexpectedly
upon them, in who knew what sort of temper after his journey,
and bearing who could guess what news on his tongue——

"Perhaps I am to go to Court," suggested Elizabeth, skipping.

But Lady Bryan would not have that either. Unseemly to put
words into the mouth of the King's messenger—the King was
busy with his new marriage plans—he had no time now for daughters at Court—theirs to bide his will until they came of a suitable
age and wisdom, to say nothing of deportment, to find favor in
his eyes——

"Who do you think it will be today?" inquired Elizabeth, al-
lowing herself to be revolved for a final inspection while her
glancing curiosity flitted back to the approaching emissary come
on his unpredictable errand from that distant splendor called
London.

Lady Bryan would not commit herself—a reddish beard, the
boy had said, and an unfriendly look withal.

"I know!" said Elizabeth, and spread her small fine hands
against the warmth of the new blaze. " 'Twill be another suitor
for Mary! She hates them so!"

Still Lady Bryan would admit nothing—and while she was
sketching in further rebukes and admonitions Dickon's tousled
head appeared cautiously at the door again.

" 'Tis Sir Thomas Wriothesley as ever is, madam—Noll spied him at the crossroads and came by the lane to warn us——"

"There, I was afraid—Sir Thomas again—so soon? What is it now, I wonder! Get along with you, boy. Away! And how many ride with him this time, in pity's name——" Lady Bryan bustled out, shooing Dickon before her.

Down into the very kitchens she penetrated, where there was soon the blubbering of a scullery maid who had blundered at the wrong minute; down to have the lids off all the pots and a finger in every pie, for she took her perilous post of governess to the King's daughters very seriously, the good woman. They kept to plain fare at Hertford, except when visitors came—there was no money for fripperies in the scanty allowance doled out from a grudging treasury for the maintenance of this half-forgotten household. But the royal messengers must be well served and fed when they came, and after they were gone the castle would dine on their leavings for days.

Sir Thomas Wriothesley, the new Secretary, with his cold manner and grim green gaze, was not a man to be lightly received. His coming meant that large matters would be afoot. He it was who had wooed by proxy for the King (unsuccessfully) the Emperor's niece Christina, Dowager Duchess of Milan—pert Christina of the famous dimples, who pointed out that she had but one head, which was not enough for a wife of the King of England. Wriothesley had not thought that very funny, but it got round in spite of him and all Europe tittered.

The King's daughters had so far little cause to love Sir Thomas Wriothesley. And now he swooped again into their defenseless lives, unheralded save by a breathless plowboy; and with some great matter, sure to be unpleasant, up his velvet sleeve.

Elizabeth, who never listened but always heard, knew a great deal about this business of Mary's marriage. Mary was twenty-three, and they were always about to marry her to somebody. Elizabeth was aware, with the critical eyes of childhood sharpened by her own ingrowing love of beauty, that Mary, sallow with years of ill-health, nearsighted, harsh-voiced, pinched and drawn with worry and grief during her mother's long martyrdom,

would not make at best a lovely bride. Elizabeth in her young
cruelness thought that they had better be quick if they meant to
find a man to love Mary. Love her? Well, marry her. Already
Elizabeth knew a great deal about state matchmaking. She was
to learn still more before her father had done with his marrying.

It was Anne of Cleves that Henry was courting now. His
fourth. Elizabeth could just remember the death of his third,
who was Edward's mother. There was a christening at Hamp-
ton Court, to which the baby prince's disinherited sisters had
been bidden. Elizabeth was four then, and she had walked in the
midnight procession from the chapel back to the Queen's chamber, holding to Mary's hand and wearing a magnificent new dress
with a train. She had got deadly tired of the torchlights and the
trumpets and the praying, but she had still a dimming memory
of the white-faced, half-fainting Queen Jane propped up on the
state pallet with cushions of crimson and gold, shivering and
sweating by turns in an ermine-lined mantle. Everyone knew
then that the Queen had almost died at Edward's birth, and the
huge King, sitting beside the pallet, was very tender in his bois-
terous way, while his wife held his hand and tried to smile
through her weakness and pain whenever he laughed—and he
was very gay, for had he not got a son at last?

And now would they make Mary a wife, the mother of a son—
and would Mary die a few days after, like Queen Jane? Dark-
eyed, the child Elizabeth regarded the simple destiny of queens:
to marry, to bear sons, and to die. Would that be Mary's brief
fate too?

They said it was Mary's duty to marry when and where and
whom her father wished her to. A princess of England, no matter
who her mother was, was a match for anyone in Europe, they
said—Elizabeth's quickened breath caught in her throat. *She was
a princess, too. . . .*

She stood there motionless on the hearth, suddenly confronted
by her own unfathomable future. Was the time to come when
the King's messenger would ride to her, as he doubtless rode now
to Mary, with an offer of marriage from a man she had never
seen, a man she might not even like? One little reddened hand

sought the tightness in her throat. Was the time to come too
when she would lie on crimson cushions and see her son come
back from the christening—a son like Edward—and she not there
for long to love him. . . .

But one must live!

Small and frightened and alone, Elizabeth of England faced a
world gone suddenly all wrong. With an odd, wild desire for escape from her own thoughts, she ran to the window, peering out
and down—Sir Thomas Wriothesley was dismounting in the
courtyard. She heard the patter of hurrying feet somewhere—a
door slammed below, a call rang out, the Secretary passed within,
his attendants at his heels, and his tired animals were led away
by Dickon and the grooms from London, who walked stiffly with
the cold. Silence lay again over Hertford Castle in the winter
sunlight.

My Lady Elizabeth's Grace turned back from the casement
with a new dignity. For the first time, with a gasp of sheer shock,
she had met panic. For the first time, in the face of panic, she
consciously achieved self-control. Sir Thomas Wriothesley must
not find a sniveling baby clutching at the window curtains and
peeping at life. He would find a princess of England, aged six.

She smoothed her hair, her dress. She stooped (painfully, in
the tight bodice) to adjust the bow on her left shoe. She looked
about for her workbasket, the treasured gift of Lady Bryan, and
sat down with it on her blue silk lap before the replenished fire,
her feet adangle from the big uncushioned chair.

From the basket she took the cambric shirt she was sewing for
Edward's New Year's gift—the stitches were as fine and even as
Lady Bryan's own. When he grew older she would stitch covers
for his books and write out fair copies of prayers he must learn,
with colored initials and tailpieces of her own devising, to draw
him on from page to page. And some day, somehow, she would
have money of her own, and make him expensive presents sewn
with pearls. . . .

The careful setting of stitches in the fine fabric steadied her,
and her first instinctive effort at royal repose was successful. Sir
Thomas Wriothesley would go to see Mary first, for she was the

eldest, and there was always this marriage business to be dealt with. Poor Mary, she would be upset, which always made her ill with headaches and pains in her teeth and palpitations of the heart. It never took much to make Mary ill.

The nightmarish moment in which she had fled blindly toward the window, an unreasoning gesture of escape from the unknown and the future, receded slowly and left her sewing by the fire, her shapely, unkept hands dainty and sure with the needle while the early winter shadows lengthened in the great paneled room.

Wriothesley found her sewing in the big chair when he had done with Mary. He was not old, and he had cultivated an ability to notice things; so his light green eyes missed nothing as she got to her feet to greet him. He saw the shabby dress, the tarnished gilt, the neatly cobbled toes of the little shoes, and the facing of a blue which did not match. He saw too the clear, level look, the high nose already royal, the fresh cap, the long, fine hands, chapped and red with cold.

All unwillingly and to his own surprise, he beheld her with approval, and was struck by a sudden heretical conviction that here was the best of King Harry's brood. Mary, with whom he had just had a most profitless interview, was sallow and sour, cherishing her mother's wrongs and her own. Edward was puffy and queer, a not altogether pleasant infant. But the child of passion and disgrace, Elizabeth, was fair and princely to look at, with an alarming candor in her straight hazel gaze beneath thin gold eyebrows and eyelashes so lightly marked as to be almost invisible. And she was Tudor through and through, bright-haired, straight-backed, and ready of tongue.

She made him a long, low obeisance, the blue silk skirt billowing about her. She made him a long, glib speech, with reference to her father's health and the filial sentiments she entertained for him; a quaint magpie rearrangement of all the drilled speeches of her little formal lifetime. Wriothesley grinned in his beard, as he had been seen to grin at young colts of promise when they were tried before him, and his sharp green eyes bored into her— he was never a man of sentiment.

When he retired to his chamber it was already twilight, and he
called for candles and sat down to write a letter to account for
this overnight delay at Hertford while Mary composed frantic
appeals to both the King and Cromwell. Wriothesley hoped he
was not being soft with Mary—and he made it quite clear in his
letter that while she might protest and plead for a time, she had
already submitted in her heart, with a resignation born of hard
experience, to her most benign and merciful father and most
gracious sovereign lord, the King.

When the real business of the day had been disposed of thus
at careful length, he paused to gnaw his pen, and his white teeth
gleamed again behind his beard. He appended a paragraph:

"I went then to my Lady Elizabeth's Grace and to the same
made the King's Majesty's most hearty commendations, declar-
ing that his Highness desired to hear of her health and sent his
blessing. She gave humble thanks, enquiring after his Majesty's
welfare, and that with as great a gravity as she had been forty
years old. If she be no worse educated than she now appeareth to
me, she will prove of no less honor and womanhood than shall be-
seem her father's daughter; whom our Lord long preserve unto
us, and send your lordship also long life many years to serve the
same."

Which was to say that Ann Boleyn's brat was a clever little
monkey, and would want watching.

[*The story of how Elizabeth was watched and of how she re-
acted are well worth reading, but for lack of space we must
reluctantly skip to the last chapter of Elswyth Thane's book.*]

Hatfield on a morning in November, and the ground was
striped with white tree-shadows of unmelted snow in the bright
sunshine. Elizabeth turned from her window and routed out two
puss-by-the-fire maids of honor, who were settling to their needlework beside the hearth. She commanded boots, and capes with
hoods, and led the way out into the crisp air.

They went along the slope of the lawn from the house toward
the avenue of oaks and bore to the right, chattering, slipping on

the frosted hummocks with little laughing squeals, making intricate tracks in the slippery whiteness, complaining cheerfully of the winter which would soon set in. Elizabeth walked between them, growing more thoughtful with each step, holding her cloak about her. The bench under the tree where they had sat to sew and read last June held a rim of rime, shaded by the close bare branches from the sun.

Elizabeth trudged on, scuffing at the turf, wondering dimly why this frosty morning seemed somehow familiar, as though she had lived it before. . . . Suddenly she halted, staring at the ground beneath her feet—it was as though dark water ran where the road began, beyond a muddy bank. For a moment only she paused there, and then moved on, clutching time about her like a cloak—ten years—ten full, comforting, terrible years, since that morning by the river. . . .

Behind them from the direction of the house came a hail, faint with distance, and the girls looked back.

"It's Mr. Cecil!" one of them exclaimed.

"He's—running!" said the other.

Elizabeth had not heard. She walked on, head bent, wrapped in her cloak, alone. The girls looked at her and at each other, large-eyed, suddenly breathless. He had been coming very often, of late, it was true, but—this time he must have left London early in the morning. . . .

"Your Grace——"

"Well?" said Elizabeth crossly over her shoulder, and walked on.

"Your Grace—do look, it's Mr. Cecil—running!"

"Cecil?" Elizabeth spun round at that, an arm flung up to shield her eyes against the sun. Cecil was coming toward them down the road, one hand at his swinging sword hilt, his cap in the other, which he waved at them—shouting—stumbling—running. Elizabeth turned back to meet him, and as she went she too—for a few steps—ran.

He flung himself on his knees when he reached her—on his knees in the cold mud of the road. He had ridden hard, and his clothes were spattered with it. He was panting.

"Your M-Majesty—!" gasped Cecil, and was seized by a spasm of coughing.

Elizabeth stood still in the muddy road, in the early sunlight, sick and giddy. Foolish to feel like this, now that it had come. One had known that it must come—any time—any minute— these days. And yet—long as one had waited—often as one had almost lost hope—*so soon?*

Her hand went out gropingly—and she felt Cecil's lips pressed hard against her knuckles. No kiss of ceremony, that. Excitement, exaltation, ran from his pounding pulses into hers. Her shoulders straightened, and her chin came up. *Majesty.* . . .

The two girls had paused discreetly, a decorous four paces to the rear, but their eyes were very round and their red mouths hung slightly open. She turned to them, white-faced, erect, seeming to their awed gaze inches taller, miles remote.

"The Queen is dead," she told them very quietly.

"G-God save the Queen!" they gasped, and curtsied where they stood.

Her eyes rested on them gravely—it was thus, under the dripping trees of Hatfield Park, from the parrot lips of two little maids-in-waiting that she first heard that mighty prayer—for herself.

Cecil had risen, and stood beside her waiting.

"Madam—we have much to do. The Chancellor will make the announcement to both Houses this morning, and the Proclamation will be read before noon at Cheapside. There will be no trouble about the accession—we may be sure of that—but orders have gone out to close the ports, in case——"

His voice went on endlessly, efficiently, as they walked back toward the house. And there, at a great oak table in the paneled parlor, they sat down with inkstands and pens and the blank white sheets of paper on which the history of England was to be written in the fine, neat hand of old Henry's sole surviving child.

Cecil spread before her from his saddlebags his lists of names, his suggestions for letters to the Continent, recommendations for new appointments abroad, memorandums as to her immediate attitude toward the Church, outlines of speeches—he had thought of everything, and had everything in readiness. Elizabeth, her head between her two slim hands, did her best to concentrate and follow what he said—she nodded and attended scrupulously, and said Yes and No at the proper points in his low-voiced, droning discourse. But at last, almost unconsciously, she singled out from the mass of written papers he had scattered across the fair white sheets still to come, a single document in a clerkly hand; and she sat staring at it, wide-eyed, fascinated, her lips parted on her breath that came and went quickly: *Elizabeth, by the Grace of God Queen of England, France, and Ireland, Defender of the Faith . . .*

"*—letters under the Queen's hand to all ambassadors with foreign princes, to authorize them therein,*" Cecil was reading from his memorandum at her elbow.

"*. . . Because it hath pleased Almighty God by calling to his mercy out of this mortal life, to our great grief, our dearest sister of noble memory, Mary, late Queen of England, France, and Ireland (whose soul God have) to dispose and bestow upon us . . .*"

"*Seven: To appoint commissioners for the interment of the late Queen,*" continued Cecil like an answering litany from his own paper. "*Eight: To appoint commissioners for the coronation, and the day. Nine: To make a continuance of the terms, with patents to the Chief Justice——*"

"*. . . We do publish and give knowledge by this our proclamation to all manner people, being natural subjects of every the said kingdoms,*" she read on, "*that from the beginning of the seventeenth day of this month of November, at which time our said dearest sister departed from this mortal life, they be discharged of all bonds and duty of subjection toward our said sister, and be from the same time in nature and law bound only to us as their only Sovereign Lady and Queen. . . .*"

She looked up into a silence, to find Cecil waiting, his eyes somewhat reproachful.

"I am listening," she said meekly, and laid down the Proclamation.

"A deputation from the Council will be here within a few hours," he remarked, "and it is necessary to have first of all some

idea of the suitable things to say when the formal announcement
of the Queen's death is made——"

"Yes, of course," she agreed, her attention pouncing at once on
this matter of an utterance which would be recorded of her for-
evermore. "There is that bit in the Psalms—yes, that is what I
want—how does it go—*A Domino factum est illud et—et—est—*"
She snapped her fingers impatiently at her own memory.

"—*et est mirabile in oculis nostris,*" smiled Will Cecil
promptly.

"Good."

"Are you sure——"

"Yes. That will do nicely. I shall say that." And then for a
moment she stared at him, troubled, with brimming eyes. "Oh,
poor Mary," she murmured, thinking of the dead Queen for the
first time that morning as a lost sister and a woman, piteous and
ill, who had died almost alone. "Poor Mary—she might have sent
for me—I should have gone——"

"It was very peaceful," said Cecil perfunctorily, for her comfort, rummaging out another paper to lay before her. "Now if I
might suggest, madam—I have here a list of the Council as it
now stands. And here another list of—I submit—suitable and
worthy men which your Majesty would do well to—consider.
The Chancellor, Pembroke, and Howard will be among the first
to reach here, I understand, when the—formalities in London are
concluded. I have heard that the Archbishop is—dying. Arundel
is still abroad at Cercamp on that matter of the Peace—they are
trying to save Calais to us, but I fear——"

"Where is Dudley?" asked Elizabeth, interrupting.

"Robert? I have no idea," said Cecil, which was not altogether
true. But the name was nowhere on any of his lists.

"I want him," she announced quietly. "Master of Horse, I
think—something like that—put him down."

There was a silence while he wrote, she watching over his
shoulder. His own name did not appear on his papers either, for
he had held no official position under Mary. Elizabeth chose a
fresh blank sheet from the pile and drew it toward her.

"Now," she said. "Now for my Privy Council." And with a

sidelong glance at him she took the pen from between his fingers, dipped it, and wrote across the top of the fair page: *Will. Cecil, Secretary of State.*

"Your Majesty——!"

"Tush, man, you expected it!" Her elbow nudged his familiarly on the table. "With Howard for Lord Chamberlain and you for Secretary—I am surely safe! We'll have Parry, too—he knows how I like things done."

"A distant connection of mine—by marriage," he acknowledged, watching in his turn while the pen set down the two names beneath his own.

"I know—he has told me so. Comptroller of the Household—there, that's for old Parry." She referred again to his list. "Who else—Arundel shall stay as he is—why not—Lord Steward." She wrote. "Such a handsome man—so gallant—so susceptible!"

"Madam——!"

"Who comes next—Pembroke—yes. Clinton—oh, yes. Winchester—?" Her brow wrinkled with doubt.

"A pliable man," he murmured. "Very—obliging."

"Well—perhaps." She wrote him slowly. "We shall see about Winchester—Lord Treasurer. Who's for Chancellor—Heath must go, for he will be a Catholic to the bitter end—besides he's very old——"

"Madam, as regards religion, I beg that you will not be hasty. In fact, I have written out——"

"One thing at a time," she insisted sharply. "Who's for Chancellor, when Heath is gone?"

And so on, while the short winter day passed its high noon, until someone brought candles; and still they sat at the long table, their heads together, their dinner cooling untasted beside them. Who was for Chancellor—who for Lord Privy Seal—in the matter of religion, better do nothing at all just yet—they must be prudent—the burnings must stop, of course—and what was to be done about the Pope—then there was her marriage—Parliament was bound to bring that up at once—and there must be a letter to Philip—this business of the Peace at Cercamp—France would offer separate terms to England now—look out for Philip there—

was there any hope of Calais—now as to the late Queen's funeral —and the new Queen's entry into London—what would she say— what would she wear. . . .

The long, wrangling, devoted partnership had begun.

On the twenty-third she rode to London, with a splendid retinue, and because the Tower was not ready for her reception she lived for nearly a week at Charterhouse. From there, along graveled streets, through crowds which laughed and cried and sang and shouted themselves hoarse, through the thunder of cannon and the ringing of church bells, she made her progress to the Tower, on horseback, wearing a purple gown. The Lord Mayor rode before, with her sceptre, while Pembroke bore the sword of state. And just behind her, magnificently mounted, gorgeously clad, rode Robert Dudley, Master of Horse.

It was past midnight of the fifteenth of January, 1559.

In the state bedchamber at Whitehall, curled snugly round the comfort of a softly wrapped hot brick in the middle of the great bed—for she had caught cold in the coronation procession from the Tower to Westminster the day before—Elizabeth lay awake.

Mary had lain in that bed, the night after she was crowned. Edward had slept there, too, a weary child of nine, on a cold night like this—had someone thought to give him a hot brick, and leave a friendly fire to smoulder on the hearth? And Henry, the great loud man who had fathered them all—well, he had died there, she supposed. And now his little red wench was Queen of England.

In the cold winter moonlight she could trace the stout oak posts of the bed rising plumply to the brooding shadows beneath the tester. Her turn now, to sleep here, and she young and strong and not afraid of anything, and with so much to do.

Her head was humming slightly from the hot mulled draught they had given her because she sneezed—the banquet had gone on and on, a delicious blur of music and red liveries and the trumpets which heralded each new course—tomorrow was the joust, and on the twenty-third she was to open her first Parliament—there was no time to be ill. She swallowed, cautiously, testing her tonsils—it hurt. There should have been more rugs in the litter—she had not foreseen so many stops and so much ceremony—but what a day it had been, clear and cold—the shouting, sobbing, loyal mobs, the flutter of pennons and streamers and waving kerchiefs, the caps tossed in the air—the pageants and speeches and tableaux, and the earnest little boys and girls, reciting poems and presenting gifts—her people, one and all, her England now.

Today, the coronation—the long blue-carpeted path to the high altar, amid the pealing bells and the voices singing *Salva feste dies*—the same blue cloth which Mary had trod only five years ago, and the bishop in hastily borrowed robes, because the state of the Exchequer required the utmost economy if there was to be any coronation at all—her own voice, strangely, repeating the Lord's Prayer alone—the gospel and epistle (read in English, at her request)—the coronation oaths, more terrible by far than the marriage vows—the oil for the anointing was nasty and it smelt—the crown was heavy and caught on her hair—the ring, made smaller, had looked very well on her white hand—(she stirred drowsily, to feel the small cool weight of it in the dark)— dear Howard, grinning in the row of peers, big with his delight and pride of her—but the homage was the best part, and had brought tears to her eyes—tall Arundel, premier earl of the land, on his knees, his hands between her hands, his daring eyes lifted to her face, her hair, her throat—such a gallant, handsome man, and not yet fifty after all—the same thrill ran through her again as she considered that he was a widower now, and openly her suitor, the last of his ancient line since the death of his only son last year—"*I become your liege man of life and limb, and of all earthly worship and faith*" . . . And at last, the thousands of voices as one, ringing to the high gray vaults of stone—"*God save Queen Elizabeth!*" Ah, but it was good, good, after all these lean years, it warmed one's blood and set one dreaming of great deeds, great triumphs, great empires. . . .

Parliament would be at her to marry, of course. Before Mary died, the King of Sweden had sent to offer his son Eric—Sweden

would certainly be heard from again, now that she was Queen—
there were tales about Eric, though—he was handsome, they said,
but bad, very bad—something of a ruffian. She was looking fas-
tidious in the dark. The Prince of Denmark was still a bachelor,
with apparently as little taste for marriage as herself—and his
uncle the Duke of Holstein was supposed to be young and
comely—the Archduke Charles of Austria had been mentioned
as an accomplished and elegant prince—and, of course, there was
Philip. Philip was already indicating his willingness to marry her
—that chilly man with the protruding gaze who had slowly murdered Mary, he and his child which never came—with Philip as
her husband she could defy the French and all this talk about
Mary Stuart—but why not defy them without him—her people
would stand behind her on that; she had no need of Philip—he
had done enough harm in England—the thing now was to keep
him out—one must be tactful, of course—one must not make an
enemy of Philip—not yet.

Anyway, she would never marry a foreigner, because see what
Mary had suffered by it. Yet if Mary had thought an Englishman
beneath the dignity of the throne—that was only Courtenay, of
course—Mary had had no such prospects as Arundel, or Howard's
son—there were unmarried English gallants aplenty now, it
seemed—a pity that Robert—with a gasp, she turned her feverish
cheeks into the pillow. Well, never mind, she could not have
married Robert anyway, she would never marry anyone, it was
much better as it was: herself on the throne, quite alone, Queen
in her own right—and behind the throne, there could still be
Robert, merry and laughing and—fond.

Parliament would make immediate difficulties about the marriage—it existed for no other purpose. She and Cecil were already
working on the speech she would make to them in reply to their
inevitable recommendation that she marry at once—*From my
years of understanding, since I first had consideration of my life,
to be born a servitor of Almighty God, I happily chose this kind
of life, in the which I yet live . . . so constant have I always
continued in this determination, although my youth and words
may seem to some hardly to agree together . . . this shall be*

for me sufficient, that a marble-stone shall declare, that a queen, having reigned such a time, lived and died a virgin. . . . Very fine. But it would not settle Parliament for long, nor stem the tide of European suitors, for no one would believe her—at first. They would see. Even Cecil did not quite believe her. Well, he would see too.

No one to compel her. Her very toes curled with the delightful knowledge. She was Queen. She was young and eager and be-loved—as her father had been at his crowning. She would not make his mistakes, and therefore they would love her to the end— but equally she would never admit to a soul that he had made mistakes. He was a great King. She would be great too. *The great-est Tudor of them all.* The phrase stirred sleepily in her mind. Well, anyway, greater than Mary—greater than Edward—yes, be-cause of all his marrying, greater even than great Henry himself.

God was very good to her. She had made a prayer and said it as she left the Tower yesterday—it was all her own, Cecil had not laid pen to it—how did it go—*O Lord Almighty and Ever-lasting God, I give Thee most humble and hearty thanks, that Thou has been so merciful unto me as to spare me to behold this joyful and blessed day—and I acknowledge that Thou hast dealt as wonderfully and as mercifully with me as Thou didst with Thy true and faithful servant, Daniel, Thy prophet; whom Thou de-liveredst out of the lion's den from the cruelty of the greedy and raging lions; even so was I overwhelmed, and only by Thee de-livered; to Thee therefore only be thanks, and honor, and praise for evermore. . . .*

And so, just short of the Amen, curled round her hot brick with one slim hand between her cheek and the pillow, Elizabeth of England slept.

ELEANOR FARJEON

Hail, Queen Elizabeth

Poets, from Shakespeare down through the intervening centuries, have written many wonderful tributes to Queen Elizabeth, calling her "Gloriana" . . . "Good Queen Bess" and many other royal nicknames.

In these few lines, a modern writer sums up the many-sided character of this amazing queen.

HAIL, Queen Elizabeth! Here comes Queen Bess
In a very big ruff and a very wide dress;
Her hair it is red, and her eyes they are green,
And England has prospered since Bess became Queen.

The boldest of sailors have sailed to the West,
The greatest of poets have written their best,
The gayest of people have danced on the green,
And England's grown merry since Bess became Queen.

From KINGS AND QUEENS, by Eleanor Farjeon and Herbert Farjeon.

84

She's vain as a peacock that opens its tail,
She's proud as an eagle that weathers the gale,
She's crafty and jealous, suspicious and mean,
But England *is* England now Bess is the Queen.

ELIZABETH GRIERSON

Mary Queen of Scots

The life of Mary Queen of Scots was a mixture of romance and melancholy. This beautiful queen, whose existence was a dangerous threat to Elizabeth I, inspired great devotion from a small group of followers who were involved with her in a series of plots and counterplots.

Theoretically, she reigned over Scotland between the years 1543 and 1587, but a large part of this time she was either at the Court of France as the child bride of the French Dauphin, or imprisoned by the English in one castle or another.

IT WAS in the afternoon of a cold October day in the year 1567 that a mud-stained rider galloped into the little town of Kinross, which lies on the western shore of Lochleven, and, throwing his horse's bridle to a servant at the tiny inn, marched down to the water's edge.

From SCOTTISH KEEPS AND CASTLES, by Elizabeth Grierson.

"A boat, a boat!" he cried imperiously; "and make haste, thou lazy loons, for I carry a letter from my Lord Regent to the Queen's Majesty."

The boatmen looked at one another in perplexity, for the speaker was no other than George Douglas, youngest brother of Sir William of that name, who was Governor of Lochleven Castle, and as such was guardian or jailer, if we care to call him so, of the lovely and unfortunate Mary Queen of Scots, who was at the time imprisoned in the island stronghold.

It was no secret to anyone who lived in the neighborhood that the young man, who had up till recently lived in the Castle, was devoted to the Queen, and was suspected, and with good reason, of planning her escape. Because of this, the Regent Moray, who had shortly before visited his royal half-sister, had ordered that he should be expelled from the Castle, and forbidden to return or to hold any communication with the unhappy captive.

Yet here he was, openly demanding a boat to take him across to the very place where by the authority of the Regent he was forbidden to go.

"But, Master George . . ." began one of the boatmen, who was instantly cut short by his impatient listener.

"I tell thee it is all right, Dickson," he cried. "See, here is my pass, signed by the Regent himself, and here is the letter bearing his own seal. But for Heaven's sake make haste—the matter brooks no delay."

Reassured by the sight of the seal on the letter, with the familiar arms of the Regent upon it, the man addressed as Dickson unshipped his oars, and the traveler was soon speeding across the narrow strip of water that separated the Castle from the mainland.

Arrived at his destination, George was received by his widowed mother, who was at that time living in the fortress, with surprised delight. For he was her youngest son and her favorite. But after listening for a few minutes to her rehearsal of the small events which had taken place during his absence, he demanded to be taken to the presence of the Queen, giving as an excuse for his impatience the urgency of the business contained in the letter.

Accordingly Lady Douglas led him across the courtyard and up to the second story of the great tower or keep, where he found his royal mistress seated at her embroidery frame.

"George!" she cried. "The saints defend thee, but how hast thou come hither? Methought thou hadst been banished by my brother's command."

"So I was, your Highness, and so will I be again," replied the young man, kneeling before his sovereign and kissing her hand, "for though my Lord Regent relaxed his ire sufficiently to entrust this letter to my hands, his heart has once more misgiven him, and if I am not mistaken there is a rider close on my heels, who was bidden to reach the Castle before me. So, as I have much to say to thee, madam, let us leave the letter for the present," and he flung it contemptuously on the table, "and turn us to plan for thine escape, while there is time."

Very hurriedly but very earnestly the two conspirators talked together, George Douglas trying to encourage the captive by telling her of the friends on shore who were scheming and plotting for her escape, and impressing on her the part she must play in the proceedings.

"I cannot be near your Highness," he went on, "but there is another whom I deem as loyal and trustworthy as myself. That is young Willie Douglas, the orphan lad who has charge of the boats. He is as deeply attached to your Majesty as his knowledge of you will allow, and if your Majesty have opportunity, and can extend a little kindness to him, the lad will serve you with all his power. And his power to serve you is greater than that of most, for he is constantly coming and going twixt the Castle and the shore. But," he added, looking through one of the deep-set windows that overlooked the loch, "our brief interview will soon be at an end, for the messenger sent by the Earl of Moray to warn Sir William against me hath reached the shore, and is already on the loch. So if your Highness has any last commands for me, they must be short."

"Short they will be," said the Queen, rising to her feet. "I will straightway make a friend of little Willie Douglas. I know the lad's face, and have oftentimes been cheered by his smile.

"And see, my trusty ally, though I have no commands, I have here two tokens to commit to thy care. One is this earring of mine; look, it is a bonny pearl, shaped like a pear, and not easily forgotten or copied. Carry it with thee, and when thy plans are matured, find an occasion to send it back to me, and then I will know to be prepared.

"This other"—and she gave him a little folded handkerchief—"is a letter to my most loyal friend, Lord Seton. Yes, you may wonder," she went on as the young man unfolded the napkin, in the hope of finding some missive wrapped up in it; "but now they allow me neither paper nor ink, so I must find some other means of script. So for ink I have the soot from the chimney, mixed with water—with practice one can write with it—while for paper I have naught to use but my finest cambric napkins which I brought with me from France."

A loud knocking at the outer gate of the Castle warned them that if the visitor were to escape, he had better depart at once. So, bidding a hasty farewell to the Queen, he slipped down the spiral staircase which led to the ground floor of the tower, let himself out by a window and so gained the rocks where the rowboats lay.

The lad we have spoken of, a rosy-cheeked, dark-haired youth of about sixteen years of age, was there alone, and it needed but a word from his young master to persuade him to let him take one of the boats across to Kinross and leave it there. Thus he managed to leave the Castle in safety ere Lord Moray's messenger had grasped the fact that he had been there at all.

To plan an escape is one thing, to carry out the plan is another! All through that winter of 1567–68, as month succeeded month in uneventful monotony, and no pearl earring found its way back into her possession, the heart of Scotland's imprisoned Queen grew heavy as lead. She had done everything in her power to help on the plans of her friends on shore. She had taken pains, by kindly words, and occasionally little presents of money, to captivate Willie Douglas, who would have gladly risked his life to do her a service. She had tried to disarm any suspicions that might be felt about an attempt to escape, by calmly discussing the possibility with old Lady Douglas, who naturally thought that if the captive had any intention of risking such an adventure, she would have guarded her secret and held her tongue.

Indeed, the suggestion was treated so much as a joke, that both soldiers and servants, tired with the isolation and monotony of their lives, often joined in a game in which the pretended rescue of the Queen played the principal part.

One evening early in April Sir William had taken his prisoner for a sail on the loch, and on their return they found the whole household thus engaged, while Lady Douglas, who was too old for such pranks, stood by looking on and laughing.

Even Queen Mary, in spite of her heavy heart, could not help smiling as she watched the attacking party, who were in boats, pelting the would-be defenders with handfuls of mud and gravel.

"Methinks there would be danger of the prisoner escaping by the rear," she said.

"Except that I should be there, your Majesty," replied Sir William rather grimly.

"I had forgotten that for the moment," rejoined the Queen lightly. "But what is that?" she exclaimed, as the report of a gun rang out from one of the boats near the shore.

"It is that fool Drysdale, firing the old harquebus which lies in the boat in order to scare the wildfowl when they come too near the shore. Pray God it be but loaded with powder and not with shot, for he fired it point-blank among the crowd. See, he hath wounded two of my men, though both the knaves seem able to limp toward the Castle. What folly is this, Drysdale?" he asked severely.

" 'Twas folly, I admit, Sir William," answered the man sheepishly, "but I had no thought than that the gun was loaded only with powder."

"And so thou hast wounded two of our best men," said his master sharply. "Let it serve as a lesson, and be done with this foolery. Let everyone go to their posts, and see to their duties," he cried, raising his voice, "and Drysdale, see thou to it that the wounded men be looked after by the Queen's chirurgeon."

The same evening that officer, who occupied a room directly

above that of his royal mistress, managed to get a word in private with her during the short half-hour when she was alone with her two maids of honor after she had supped.

"Your Majesty," he began bluntly, "I now have it in my power to give you an opportunity which it behoves you to make use of. It happens that these two men whom Drysdale in his clumsiness hath so opportunely wounded are the leaders of those who are always watching your every action and spying on your friends.

"Each of them hath a bullet in his leg, and, by'r Lady, it will not be my fault if their recovery is not slow and tedious, or if they leave their beds as long as it is to your advantage to have them left there."

"A thousand thanks for thy good offices, my friend," replied Mary sadly. "If I could get speech with George Douglas, we might maybe hatch some plot; but I have not had a word from him since before Yule."

"I heard a rumor two days ago that George Douglas, vexed by his banishment from Lochleven, was going to France," said the chirurgeon, "but I do not know if it is false or true."

"God grant it may be false," replied the Queen, tears coming into her eyes, "for if George Douglas leaves the country, then is my case hopeless indeed."

The rumor proved to be true, to all appearance at least, for some days later Lady Douglas entered the Queen's apartment in great agitation, holding an open letter in her hand.

"I have come to crave thine aid, your Majesty," she cried. "My luckless son hath sent me this letter to tell me that, tired of all the plotting and intrigue in this land, he hath determined to try his fortunes at the Court of France."

The Queen smiled sadly at the old lady's words. "But what can I, a helpless prisoner, do to prevent thy son's going abroad?" she asked.

"Perchance if your Majesty would write him a letter, begging him to remain in Scotland, he would listen to your words. I can send it with my own," said Lady Douglas, completely forgetting that in disobeying the strict injunction of the Regent that her youngest son should have no communication with the Queen, she was hardly acting fairly to her eldest son, Sir William, who was responsible for the safekeeping of that royal lady.

Write to George Douglas! At the thought of having the chance of so doing, the color rose in Mary's cheeks, and she had much ado to keep her voice from trembling, for she had arranged a simple cipher with him, so that, while appearing to write an ordinary letter which anyone could read, she could in reality convey a far different message.

Accordingly a letter was written by the royal hand, and, after having been read by Lady Douglas and her son, was dispatched with that of the former to the impatient young man, now lingering in the neighborhood of Kinross. He took no notice of that of the Queen, but wrote affectionately to his mother, stating that if she wanted to say farewell to him she must make an opportunity to meet him in the little town, immediately, as he intended to set out for France within four days.

So the poor old lady was rowed across to Kinross, and there took a sorrowful farewell of her son. As they parted he pulled a little packet wrapped loosely in dirty paper out of his pocket. Opening it, he displayed a pear-shaped earring.

"One of the boatmen found this on the shore of the island and brought it to me, offering to sell it," he said, "but I knew it belonged to the Queen. She must have dropped this one when setting out for a sail with my father. Wilt thou return it to its owner, with my respects and the offer of my service."

"Much good thy service will do her with the sea betwixt thee," retorted Lady Douglas sharply. Nevertheless she took the earring and deposited it in one of her capacious pockets. When she arrived at the Castle she went straight to the Queen's apartment.

"Now, well-a-day! the headstrong lad hath gone," she sobbed, "and God alone knoweth when I shall see him again. Alack, your Majesty!" she added, "though I ken that it was the nobles' will that you should return to your native land, I find myself wishing many a time that you had bidden in France."

"And many a time I find myself wishing the same," replied Mary sadly.

"Forgive me, madam," she said, "for being my father's daughter, for that was the beginning of the whole trouble." Her voice was so wistful that tears rose unbidden in the older woman's eyes, and she thrust her hand hurriedly into her pocket, seeking her handkerchief. Along with it she grasped the little packet her son had given her.

"Preserve me! but I was forgetting," she cried, pulling it out and drying her eyes. "Look what a boatman found. Did you not mark its loss? The rascal tried to sell it to my son, but he knew it as yours. He entrusted it to me to be given to you with the offer of his lasting service. Much good, I told him, that would do you, while he was in France and you in Lochleven Castle."

For a moment Mary could not trust herself to answer, but light seemed to have come into the gloomy chamber and joy into her heart. Here was a token that George Douglas was *not* going to France. For had it not been arranged that the earring was to be returned only to warn her to be ready?

To gain time to collect her thoughts, she stood for a moment turning the ornament over and over in her hand. "It was good of him to be so mindful," she said at last, her voice quite steady now, "for I would have grieved had I lost this. It belonged to my grandmother of Guise.

"When doth your son set out for France?" she added, speaking quite casually.

"When he actually takes boat I know not, but he mentioned that he was riding to Glasgow tomorrow night."

"Riding to Glasgow tomorrow night!" Once more the quick color flashed into Mary's face. For those were the words that had been agreed on to let her know the day and hour when she must hold herself ready for the great adventure.

She was glad when her kindly old visitor bade her good-night, and her two waiting-maidens came into the room, evidently greatly excited over some unwonted happening.

"Something unusual must be afoot, your Majesty," said Janet Kennedy, the elder of the two, "for young Willie Douglas hath bidden the whole household, from the Governor and old Lady Douglas down to little Margaret, who is but six years old, to a *déjeuner* tomorrow at midday, after which the maddest revels have to take place, Willie himself acting the part of the Abbot of Misrule. For some reason, the feast is not to be held in the great hall, but in the smaller guestchamber on the other side of the courtyard. Sir William hath given his consent to Willie's request.

"But, your Majesty"—and here the young girl lowered her voice—"if Willie Douglas hath no other meaning than a simple revel he is an impudent varlet, for he bade me seek your Highness's ear, and whisper into it that he hath need of siller to carry out his plan."

"And siller he shall have," said the Queen, opening a casket in which, concealed in a secret drawer, was a considerable sum of money. "Here, Janet, give this to him secretly—secretly, I say— for thou knowest not—indeed I know not myself—how much hangs upon his plan. And now, my maids, let us talk of other matters, for it will soon be time to sup, and supper often brings, as thou knowest, an evening visit from our jailer, Sir William."

Sure enough, Sir William appeared with the evening meal, which the Queen, as a special favor was allowed to partake of in her own room. He told his prisoner, in his ponderous way, of the morrow's festivities, and explained that Willie had begged that the *déjeuner* should be set in the smaller guestchamber, as he wished to prepare various little surprises for his guests. This explanation appeared to satisfy the simple mind of Sir William, but the Queen's quicker wits saw at once another reason. For while the window of the great hall looked straight across to Kinross, the windows of the guestchamber looked away in the other direction, and from them nothing was visible but a wide expanse of wood and water.

By noon next day the whole of the inhabitants of the Castle were in wild excitement. Willie had certainly played his part well, and provided, not only an excellent meal, but many new-fangled surprises and frolics.

There was a fortune-teller, whom no one could recognize, who claimed that he could unfold the future; and there was a necromancer, who looked like the Evil One himself.

Finally, there was a search all over the Castle for "hidden treasure," which turned out to be two merks hidden in a snuff-mull under the root of an old thorn tree in the garden. It was while they were searching for this that the Master of the Revels managed to cross the Queen's path and whisper to her in passing that she should be ready to slip down the stairs and leave the Castle with one of her waiting-maids, while the household were at supper. "I've borrowed some countrywoman's clothes," he muttered; "Janet Kennedy will find them lying in an old cask in the cellar; put them on, and let Janet watch from the window for my signal. If I have managed to get the key I will hold up my right hand. If I hold up my left then your Highness must make shift to get out of the window. I will set two oars up against it, which may serve in lieu of a ladder."

Mary took part in the revels as long as possible, then, feeling her need of rest, for she had not closed an eye the night before, she withdrew to her chamber, accompanied by young Lady Douglas, for she was seldom left alone. She threw herself on her bed, and the Mistress of the Castle, seeing that she was inclined for conversation, called in the old woman who kept the inn at Kinross, and sat down to indulge in a good gossip.

Mary took little notice of the talk at first, but her attention was aroused by hearing George Douglas named.

"Aye, he is still in the neighborhood, your Ladyship. I saw him yesterday with my Lord Seton and my Lord Beaton, who were passing through Kinross on their way to the Assize Court at Glasgow," said the old innkeeper. "Folk have said that my Lord Beaton and my Lord Seton were at daggers drawn, but they must have found some way of composing their differences."

Well did Mary know what it was that had induced these haughty noblemen to sink their differences and join together in a mutual endeavor. It was loyalty to her person, it was in order to effect her escape!

The knowledge that they were actually in the neighborhood, waiting and watching for the boat that would bring her ashore, was almost too much for her. She felt that she must go outside and see what was to be seen on shore.

"I would fain take the air," she said, "for I have a sore throbbing in my temples."

"In good sooth, your Majesty looks flushed and feverish," replied young Lady Douglas, looking at her anxiously.

"No, it is not a fever, it is merely that this chamber is hot now that the sun beats on the windows. My cheeks will cool once I am in the fresh air."

Old Lady Douglas joined the Queen in the garden, for she was not allowed to go beyond the courtyard unattended, and together they paced up and down the terrace which looked across to the little town of Kinross.

"Do my eyes deceive me? Or is yon a body of horsemen?" cried the old lady suddenly. "Hey! there is no doubt of it, I saw the sun glinting on their armor as they came out of the wood. See, they are riding toward Kinross—there must be twenty of them. I must raise an alarm, someone must go ashore at once, for dear only knows what their purpose may be."

The Queen looked in the direction in which the excited old woman was pointing, and was just in time to see the last of a body of soldiers disappearing behind a low hill. Quick as thought she set herself to change the conversation and to divert the old lady's mind.

"If there is an Assize at Glasgow, doubtless many riders are abroad," she replied carelessly, and then she began to inquire about tales of long ago, when Lady Douglas was young, and she herself a child at Inchmahome, and the older woman was soon quite absorbed in bygone memories, quite forgetful of what might be passing on shore. For over an hour they paced up and down, and the old lady was quite astonished, though the clever Queen was not, when Sir William came toward them with the news that her Majesty's supper was served, and that he had been waiting some time to escort her to her room.

Here another danger awaited her, for Sir William, happening to glance out of the window, discovered Willie Douglas just below him busily engaged in examining, or so it seemed to him, the chains by which the boats were moored to the little pier.

"What art thou doing there, thou fool? The boats are fast enough and do not need thy meddling. Be off at once, it is almost dark, and no time for a smatchet like thee to be fiddling with the chains."

A chill of fear gripped Mary's heart. She knew what Willie Douglas was about, for they had spoken of such an enterprise, when they had little hope of ever being able to carry it out. He was putting wooden pegs into the fastening of the chains of all the boats but one, so that, when the Queen's escape was discovered and pursuit organized, it would be very difficult to unfasten them.

Once more her quick wit came to her aid. "Oh, Sir William!" she exclaimed, sinking back on the settle in the corner farthest from the window, "methinks these revels have been too much for me, for first my head was hot and heavy, and now I am as cold as lead, and like to fall into a swoon. Send one of my maidens, an it please thee, for a cup of wine."

Sir William gazed wildly about for one of the two waiting-maids, for he was none too fond of attending to swooning women, but neither maid was there. Of course the Queen knew that. So he was fain to go himself—and by the time he had returned and the Queen had drunk the wine, the question of what Willie Douglas was doing had gone clean out of his head.

He served the Queen ceremoniously while she supped, then went to join the rest of the household at their evening meal in the great hall below, leaving his little daughter and her cousin with the royal party, a very usual arrangement, for it was felt that the quick eyes of these children would notice any unusual happenings in the room.

But the Queen had already planned how to escape from their curious eyes. As we have seen, the room directly above hers was occupied by her chirurgeon, and she had directed Janet Kennedy to take the clothes provided by Willie Douglas up to this apartment, and to confide to him the news that an escape was to be attempted that evening. As he supped with the household, his chamber would be empty just when the Queen required it, and, by keeping his eyes open and his wits alert, he could perhaps help Willie Douglas in whatever plans he had laid to obtain possession of the keys of the Castle.

Accordingly, when the clatter of dishes let her know that the party below had commenced supper, she announced that she wished to say her evening prayers as she intended to go early to bed, and, as the chirurgeon was absent from his room and it was quieter there, she would go upstairs for a little time with Janet Kennedy, while Maria Courcelles would stay with the little girls, and have a game of tod-in-the-hole. The children, delighted at this arrangement, for they loved the game, and quite accustomed to the Queen's habit of observing stated times of prayer, settled down on each side of the good-natured Maria, while Queen Mary and Janet sped noiselessly upstairs, and arrayed themselves hastily in the dark-colored kirtles and hoods which turned them into a couple of countrywomen.

Meanwhile, down in the hall, supper was proceeding as usual. At the head of a small table set on a dais sat Sir William Douglas, the keys of the Castle, five of them, hung on a chain, lying on the table beside him, for as the members of the guard supped with the rest of the household at this hour, it was the custom that the outer doors and gates should be locked and the keys brought into the hall. Beside him sat his wife and other relatives, also the Queen's medical attendant. The other inhabitants of the Castle, soldiers, servants, and boatmen, supped at the great table below the dais, in the center of the hall.

The first course was eaten among genial jokes and laughter, for the day's revels had put everyone in good humor. Then came the second course, and Willie Douglas, waiting at the Governor's table, brought in a massive dish of stewed capons. As a well-trained page, he carried a napkin over his left arm, and as he set down the capons before his master the napkin slipped from his arm and dropped, as if by accident, on the keys, a corner of it falling into the gravy in the dish. The chirurgeon, whose keen eyes noticed the incident, instantly began to talk with great earnestness about some points of medicine, in which he knew Sir William was interested, and that good man, who was peculiarly unsuspicious, joined in the conversation with such intense interest that he forgot, for the moment, the tasty dish steaming under his nose. Meanwhile, the page, with great deliberation, though, if anyone had noticed it, with a very shaky hand, drew the corner of the napkin out of the dish, and, crumpling it together, retired quickly from the hall, as if to go in search of a clean one. Meanwhile the conversation between the chirurgeon and the Governor grew more and more animated; everyone was listening, so the incident passed unheeded.

Upstairs in the chirurgeon's room two women, clad in country hoods and kirtles, over which were thrown long dark cloaks, stood counting the minutes with trembling breath. Janet Kennedy was by the tiny window, the Queen beside the half-open door. Up the staircase came the sound of the merry voice of Maria Courcelles, playing with the children; farther away still sounded faintly the voices in the great hall.

"He is out—he has given the signal," whispered Janet. "Let us go at once, and may the saints aid and defend us!"

Swiftly and noiselessly the two shadowy figures slipped down the winding newel staircase, past the room where Maria and the two little Douglases were, past the hall with its loud voices and rattle of dishes, through the deserted entrance hall littered with pieces of armor and weapons of sport, and out of the great door, beside which Willie was standing, and which he locked behind them with a sigh of relief.

"I oiled it last night," he muttered, as they stole down the rocky shore to where the boats were moored. "I rose at midnight when the guards were all asleep."

In another moment they were in a boat and had cast off from the island, Willie pulling one oar, Janet another, while the Queen lay in the stern so as to be hidden from observation. When they had rowed about a furlong out, Willie drew the keys from his pocket, and flung them into the loch. "'Twill be long enough before they lay hands on these again." He laughed. "And, as all the doors are locked, it will take Sir William and his men some little time to find a way out of the Castle. Doubtless they will jump out of the windows, but most of them are barred, and even when they do, I have taken good care that they will find the boats ill to launch. I drove a gimlet twice through the bottom of each of them, as well as fouling the chains."

"Stand up, your Majesty," he said presently, "and wave to the shore. For there are watchers there waiting to make sure you are in the boat ere they give the signal to the horsemen who are gathered in readiness up there on the hillside."

With a glad little cry, Mary sprang to her feet, and, standing in the prow of the boat, drew forth her white veil bordered with crimson and gold, which had been hidden by the dark hood, and waved it above her head, tears of joy running down her cheeks meanwhile. Instantly a man, who seemed to have been lying on his face on the shore, sprang to his feet, and gave a signal to someone in the rear. Then a rider was seen to spring to his saddle and gallop away in the evening mist.

The main body of men could not have been far distant, for, as the boat approached the land, little groups of horsemen came galloping down from all directions, their heads uncovered, their daggers drawn.

George Douglas was there, eager to be the first to greet his Queen. Lord Beaton was there, and Lord Seton, and Lord Herries, and the gallant Master of Sempill, husband of Mary Livingstone, who had been one of the Queen's Maries.

"But how could so many men gather?" asked Mary in amazement. "I expected one or two, but methinks this is a little army, well-nigh a hundred strong."

"The good folk of Kinross are loyal to your Highness," replied Willie proudly, "and many have risked the vengeance of your enemies by harboring your friends 'neath their roofs these two nights past. Aye, and they have sheltered the horses in stables for ten or twenty miles round, and given them what old oats they had, so that they may be fit and ready for hard riding."

As he spoke, the boat grated on the gravel of the shore, and willing hands drew her in. Disdaining their help, the Queen jumped ashore, and, half crying, half laughing with excitement and joy, held out her hand for her triumphant followers to kiss. But there was little time for ceremony. At any moment pursuit from the Castle might begin, and, although the Queen was once more free, she was surrounded by danger on every hand.

A number of horses, the fleetest that could be found in the length and breadth of Scotland, stood ready, and Mary and her companions were soon mounted, and, with the loyal nobles at their sides and surrounded by their followers, rode briskly through the little town, the simple townsfolk crowding to their doorways and crying blessings on the Queen as she passed. Once in the open country, they set spurs to their horses, and, ere night had completely fallen, the fair young Queen of Scots, for even now she was only twenty-five, was safely lodged in the Castle of West Niddrie in Fife, the seat of the Earl of Seton.

HELEN O'CLERY

Sea Queen of Ireland

Ireland was by tradition a land of rebels. Queen Elizabeth found that out when Granuaile, Queen of Connaught, refused to pay tribute to her Deputy in Galway. Granuaile was a Sea Queen whose pirate fleet operated in the Atlantic Ocean. She was the only Irish queen who ever reigned in her own right. In fact there was no Irish law which permitted her to do so, but Granuaile was a law unto herself.

In this story, two of her numerous grandchildren have escaped from Dublin Castle where they were held by the English, and have made their way home.

ALL THE NEXT DAY the castle of Granuaile, Sea Queen of Connaught, was astir with welcome for Grace and Donal. Everyone wanted to hear of their adventures. Granuaile said there was no harm in telling the story, and the twins were treated as heroes.

From THE REBEL SEA QUEEN, by Helen O'Clery.

People said that before long the bards would be singing ballads and reciting sagas about the adventures of the youngest O'Malleys, who had escaped from prison in Dublin, where their father was still held as hostage.

Then Granuaile took a bold step. She sent an invitation to Sir Richard Bingham and his officers to come to a feast in her castle in honor of her grandchildren.

The boldness of this move made both the Irish and the English gasp. Bingham, suspecting a plot, hesitated to accept, for though Granuaile's castle was surrounded by his soldiers, a formidable number of Irish warriors were still inside. But since Murrough O'Malley was in Dublin Castle and would be killed if his mother broke faith, Bingham accepted. He wondered about Granuaile's brazen gesture, but decided that despite her reputation she was merely a foolish woman, so happy to have her grandchildren home that she must tell the world.

There were also many inside the castle who wondered what Granuaile had in mind. None of her followers made the mistake of thinking that sentiment had run away with her common sense. However, all agreed that Granuaile was playing a dangerous game, and they wondered what she was planning. Even Grace and Donal were surprised, but they looked forward to the next move, which they were sure would be exciting.

Meanwhile, preparations for the feast proceeded. Wine that had been successfully hidden from the English was now brought forth. Oxen, venison, and fowl suddenly appeared from a countryside supposedly bare of provisions. The servants sang as they worked. All through the castle, in spite of a slight uneasiness in the air, there was eager anticipation of the unexpected feast.

Grace and Donal, dressed in their best clothes, appeared for the first time in months as a real prince and princess, even though Grace's dark hair was still somewhat shorter than was considered dignified.

Bingham and his officers arrived promptly at the castle and were escorted into the reception room by Granuaile, who formally presented the twins. Sir Richard expressed surprise at their youth and asked them to tell him of their adventures, which they did with a seemingly simple innocence. He tried to conceal his annoyance when he learned that over and over again he had been tricked by them.

Grace and Donal, as the guests of honor this night, sat near Bingham and continued to entertain him with hair-raising tales of Granuaile's many exploits.

As the evening wore on, everyone became merry. At length, Bingham suggested that all the important guests should come aboard his ship, which was anchored in the bay. He had some very good Spanish wine aboard, he said, and they could continue the party there.

"No, thank you, sir." And Granuaile laughed. "I have been a guest aboard your ship before, and ended in a Galway dungeon. But why not come aboard my flagship at Clare Island? She has better wine in her holds than you will find anywhere this side of France."

Bingham studied Granuaile for a moment, wondering if she did not remember that her ships were now manned by his sailors and that the French wine in their holds had long since disappeared. She gazed back at him with so innocent an expression that he did not mention it.

Grace and Donal, looking from one to the other, could not guess what lay behind their grandmother's bland smile.

"Very well," Bingham said. "If you will not show trust in me, I shall show trust in you. We will sail together across Clew Bay and continue this party in the flagship of the great Irish Queen." He rose grandly and walked toward the door, offering his arm to Granuaile, who accepted it with a quiet smile. His followers and hers followed them in troubled silence.

Down by the outer harbor they boarded a waiting boat. Donal and Grace slipped into it unnoticed, but most of the others were left behind to follow in other boats.

It was a calm night and while Granuaile entertained Bingham, the twins looked closely at the passengers. The only obvious Englishman aboard, besides the governor, was Bingham's personal attendant. The oarsmen all had their backs to the passengers, but as Donal watched them heaving to and fro, he suddenly felt certain that most of them were Irish.

When they reached the harbor at the back of Clare Island, they rowed straight to Granuaile's flagship. Everyone went aboard. Liveried attendants offered refreshment. Bingham allowed Granuaile to play the hostess, and did not ask where she had obtained the wine. But soon he began to feel uneasy because so few of his followers were aboard.

He rushed out on deck and scanned the sea, but no other boats had put out from the shore. He returned to Granuaile and asked her sharply what had caused the delay.

"How should I know?" she answered innocently. "Perhaps they are enjoying the party ashore too well to drag themselves away. Let us enjoy ourselves here and forget about them."

"No!" he shouted, suspecting that Granuaile was silently laughing at him. "You have walked into my power for the second time, and again we shall make haste for Galway!"

His shouted commands to his captains and officers were immediately obeyed. Oarsmen rowed the vessel out of the harbor, and as soon as they were in open sea they set the sails.

Noting that other ships of Granuaile's fleet followed at a discreet distance, Bingham frowned. Grace and Donal realized that an escort was not part of the Englishman's plan.

Granuaile stood in the bows, her long black hair ruffled by the wind and her white embroidered dress and blue cloak rippling behind her. She seemed not a warlike chieftainess today, but a peaceful queen. As she gazed at the receding coast, her eyes seeking out each peak, bay, and beach in turn, her grandchildren tried to guess her thoughts.

Grace and Donal felt sad as one familiar landmark after another slid past, until finally the city of Galway came into view. From the mouth of the bay it looked exceptionally beautiful with its domes, spires, and marble buildings. But the twins remembered the cold, dank dungeons underground, and could scarcely help wondering if they would all soon be there again.

Bingham called out triumphantly to the sailors to alter course and sweep into the bay. But no change was made in the setting of the sails, and the twins, with growing puzzlement, suspected mutiny. Again Bingham shouted orders, and again they were ignored.

Then Granuaile turned and called out, "Heave to!"

Immediately the huge ship was turned into the wind, and as her sails began to flap she lost speed until she seemed to be going backward.

Bingham roared in fury. Then he reached for his sword to strike the first person who dared ignore his command. But before the blade was out of its scabbard, two sturdy seamen seized and held the Governor, his arms by his sides.

"Lower a boat," Granuaile commanded.

Immediately a small boat was put into the water. Bingham struggled furiously with his captors, shouting counterorders.

"The tables have been turned, dear sir," Granuaile said. "You thought that my ships were manned by your men. But while you ate and drank at my table a changeover took place. Not a shot was fired, as you and I agreed. Just a little something went into the wine! Your lads will waken on a Clare Island hilltop tomorrow morning."

She stopped to laugh. "But by then it will be too late to follow. *This* time, dear Governor, you are an honored guest of mine. But instead of consigning you to a dungeon, I am sending you home. There, being lowered into the small boat, is your trusted attendant; you will follow him presently and he no doubt will row you to Galway in due course."

As Granuaile spoke, the English flag was hauled down and the blue pennant of the O'Malleys was raised.

Bingham scowled, but realizing that he had been outwitted, he turned with dignity to the chair waiting to lower him into the boat far below.

"Au revoir, *Madame*," he said with a mock bow. "You win this round, perhaps. But the trump cards lie with me."

"Do not be so sure," Granuaile answered. "You may find that they have been conjured out of your hand."

"Even you, for all your impudence, cannot dare to hope that you will get the better of me while I hold the Queen's commission," Bingham shouted back from his seat in the rowboat.

"I am Queen of Connaught. You hold no commission from me," Granuaile replied.

Her galley came round into the wind, its sails billowing, and the flagship of the O'Malleys swept away from the tiny boat that was to take the governor of Galway ashore.

Grace and Donal watched the little boat until it dwindled to a speck drifting toward the towers and domes that gleamed in the early morning sun. They wondered if ever Granuaile would drive out the English and reign in one of those marble palaces herself. Then they noticed that their ship had not turned for home, but was sailing down the coast of Clare, keeping well out from the mainland.

"We're off on some adventure!" Donal cried. "I wonder if we're going in search of English pirates."

His eyes shone as he gazed into the far distance, hearing in his imagination the boom of cannon, seeing the smoke and smelling the gunpowder.

"That is all over now." Grace brought her brother down to earth by reminding him that after Granuaile's last fierce sea encounter with the English, Bingham had offered to make peace with the Irish. He had invited all the local chieftains to a banquet in Galway, to discuss the matter and also to draw up an agreement.

"But Father was the only one who trusted him," Donal said. "The others all claimed that a treaty signed by Bingham was not worth the paper it was written on. How right they were, except that Bingham didn't even bother to draw up the treaty. He just threw his guest into prison. I wonder if Father is sorry now that he didn't take Uncle Richard's advice?"

"I don't think so," Grace replied. "Father can be as determined in his own way as Uncle Richard. He believes in achieving peace by peaceful methods, just as firmly as Uncle Richard believes that only force can keep the enemy at bay."

"I wonder who is right," Donal mused, a puzzled frown on

his face. "And I wonder where we're going now. One thing is certain, we're not heading for home."

"You are right." Granuaile came toward them to make this announcement. "We are going to England to see Queen Elizabeth. Your father was correct when he said that it was time someone told her what was going on over here, all in her name. Since he was prevented from going himself, we will go instead."

All that day, as they sailed down the west coast of Ireland, the twins remained on deck. They gloried in the wind, the sea, the distant blue hills on the landward side, and the fact that they were aboard Granuaile's galley, voyaging to unknown adventures. From time to time they wondered about London and about Queen Elizabeth's court. Then a sea gull would wheel above them against the blue sky. A sailor high in the crow's nest would call out *All clear*, or a summons below for food would recall them from daydreams into the even more exciting present.

On the second day out, they left the coast of Ireland. Their next sight of land would be the southwesternmost tip of England. The twins had never been so far out to sea before, remote from everything except the escort ships that kept far ahead and far astern, maintaining a lookout. Suddenly a signal from one of them reported, "Sails on our port bows."

Granuaile mounted to the bridge almost before the signal was read. She gave instructions to alter course immediately and sent orders to the escort ships to do likewise. Soon they were heading toward the coast of France. The wind was growing stronger and the sea was getting rough.

"I hope we're not in for a storm," Granuaile said, glancing at the racing clouds ahead.

Grace and Donal looked at her in surprise. She had ridden out more storms than they could count, and had always seemed to glory in it.

"We have no time to spare for storms," she said in answer to their unspoken question.

"But why are we in such a hurry?" Donal asked. "And if we're in a hurry, why didn't we go by land to Dublin, across the narrow strip of water to Wales, and overland from there to London?"

"One question at a time," Granuaile chided him. "Yet, perhaps the answer to both questions is the same," she said. "Bingham will guess that we are bound for London, and that the story we will tell his Queen won't do him any good. If we had gone overland, he'd have managed to intercept us somewhere. But on sea he cannot overtake us. Remember that when we left, his fleet was still in Clew Bay, his crews asleep on a hilltop, so we have at least two days' head start."

"*Could* he get there before us?" Grace asked.

"If we were delayed, he might get there first. But given a fair wind and no obstacles, we should be there before him. So, if he is as wise as he is cunning, he will not try to race us to London. If we win, he should avoid coming within range of Elizabeth's tongue *and* the Tower of London."

A sudden squall blew up, starting the canvas chattering so loudly nothing else could be heard. The ship tossed and rolled. Spray surged over the bows, splashing the twins' faces and wetting their clothes. They could have gone below for shelter, but they preferred to stay where they were, laughing as shower after shower splashed over them. Their grandmother made signs to her crew when the clatter of the storm was too great for words to be heard.

As the day wore on, the weather worsened. They played chess for a while, trying to pretend that they did not notice the storm, but after their chessmen had been thrown to the floor for the third time, they gave up. Food was brought to them, but they did not feel hungry. Their bunks were readied for the night, but they did not feel sleepy.

Before dawn the wind had blown itself out. Later in the day they turned northward again, heading straight for England. Carefully avoiding the Goodwin Sands, on which they could see the remains of many wrecks, they entered the Thames estuary.

It would be almost too much to expect that they could get all the way to London without challenge from an English ship; yet they nearly did. They were within sight of the Tower itself, and had sent their escort ships ahead to announce their arrival and to deliver letters to the English Queen, when a large galley pulled out from the riverside and fired a salvo of shots into the air.

Granuaile ordered her oarsmen to backwater. Sails had already been lowered, for the wind was from the wrong direction for going upriver. The Irish ship came to a standstill, and the English vessel pulled alongside it in midstream. A gangway was lowered from deck to deck and a young man dressed in a most elegant doublet and hose stepped onto Granuaile's ship.

Donal nudged Grace, who smiled back at her brother, but neither of them spoke. The English nobleman bowed to Granuaile and bade her welcome to London. He said that he himself had only recently returned from Dublin, that the Queen had sent for him, as she was making inquiries into certain matters concerning Ireland. Granuaile, he said, could not have come at a better moment, and the Queen would receive her. Meanwhile, he, Captain Fortescue, was at her service and would have the pleasure of escorting her to apartments which had been placed at her disposal.

The drive through London in an open coach was thrilling to the twins. The city, unlike anything they could ever have imagined, was bewilderingly big, with narrow streets twisting in all directions. There were huge palaces, even more magnificent than those of Galway, but there were also people living in hovels, overcrowded and poverty-stricken, and this the children had never seen before. Beggars in the streets held out their bony hands for alms, and magnificent coaches swept by, drawn by beautiful horses and driven by liveried coachmen.

The next day, with much pomp and ceremony, the Irish visitors were ushered into the presence of Queen Elizabeth. Fascinated by the court and by the Queen's appearance, the twins almost forgot the curtsies, bows, and obeisances which they had so carefully rehearsed.

Granuaile and Elizabeth sat opposite to each other at a magnificent table inlaid with gold, discussing affairs of state while their subjects stood nearby awaiting their pleasure.

How very much alike they are, thought Grace, yet in many

ways how different. That they were born in the same year, she already knew. One had hair as dark as a raven, the other flaming red. One wore a gown of satin, embroidered with jewels and spun gold. The other wore velvet fashioned in the latest extravagant style and embroidered with pearls. Both were tall and stately. They sat erect, their hands folded on their laps.

As they talked, neither conceded a point without due argument. Granuaile had been to visit Queen Elizabeth at least once before, and they seemed to have taken up their friendship again where they had left off. From time to time the two queens raised their voices till they could be heard across the vast room.

"Shall I make you a countess?" Elizabeth was saying. "Then Bingham might listen with more respect."

"I have no need of English titles," Granuaile retorted. "But perhaps you would like me to bestow an Irish title upon you?"

A shocked gasp went through Elizabeth's retinue at these words, but unmindful of them, Granuaile went on. "All I require of you is a signed warrant for the release of my son, who is held unjustly in Dublin Castle. Then I guarantee to make Bingham listen to me in language he understands."

Elizabeth looked at Granuaile in silent amusement while she considered the meaning of these words. "I prefer you as a friend than as an enemy," she said. "But enough for today. We shall talk again tomorrow."

Grace and Donal did not always accompany Granuaile when she went to visit Elizabeth. After the first few times they were relieved to find that they were no longer required at court, where they had been allowed only to stand, listening when they could. The battle of wits between the two queens was fascinating when they could follow it, but they could not go close enough to hear very much.

Granuaile did not hesitate to tell Elizabeth what she thought of Bingham and his unjust rule. He had remained in Galway, but he had sent dispatches in which he had said that his actions were "safety precautions to keep the wild Irish under control." He had described Granuaile as a "she-pirate who is untamable, despite her smooth tongue and varied excuses." There was a half-truth in this description which required explaining, for in the days before Murrough had been taken as a hostage, Granuaile had retaliated by plundering Bingham's ships whenever Bingham had plundered her castles or her lands.

The talks continued. The queens seemed to be enjoying themselves, but Grace and Donal were glad when Captain Fortescue offered to take them to the playhouse instead. This sounded promising. Neither of the children had seen a play before, whereas diplomatic arguments were no novelty to them.

"That would be wonderful!" said Donal. He and his sister loved all sorts of entertainment. At home they had seen pageants, dancing and mime, jugglers and conjurers. They had listened enthralled to storytelling and ballad singing. But though they had heard of plays, in which the actors used both speech and action to tell their story, they never had seen such a performance.

"We'll go to the Globe Theatre this very night," Captain Fortescue declared. "Run along now and dress for the theater. To see William Shakespeare acting in one of his own plays will help to complete your education."

During the following days, they saw *Julius Caesar, Macbeth,* and *Coriolanus,* and each time were even more enthralled than before.

"Some day I'm going to write plays about Granuaile and her great sea victories," Donal declared, as they drove home on the fourth night.

"I'd like to write plays about the things happening around us," Grace said.

"An excellent idea," said Captain Fortescue, "and one with which William Shakespeare himself would agree. But, unfortunately, even when people see each other's point they don't always act on it. That's why you are leaving London on the next tide."

"Leaving London?" echoed the twins, utterly dismayed.

"I wish you could stay longer," Captain Fortescue said. "But now that Granuaile has secured the warrant for your father's release—"

"The warrant? Then father can come home at last!"

"Yes," Captain Fortescue replied. "He can go home—if you get him out of Dublin Castle before Queen Elizabeth changes her mind and revokes the warrant."

"But surely, once she has given her word she won't go back on it?" Donal protested.

"She could change her mind six times in one night," Captain Fortescue replied with a smile. "She is a queen and does what she likes."

"But a queen should know her mind," Grace said.

"It is not quite as simple as it sounds," Captain Fortescue replied. "For example, suppose Shakespeare were to write a play about Granuaile and Bingham. He could give a true picture of the Irish Sea Queen's visit to her English rival and of their long talks. He could show how Queen Elizabeth learns that some of her representatives in Ireland had deliberately stirred up trouble so that they could plunder the rebellious chieftains' property under the pretext of keeping the peace. When Elizabeth sees this clearly for the first time, she is furious with the men who have misused her authority. And then, grateful to Granuaile for making her aware of the situation, and in the hope of repaying Granuaile, she signs the warrant for your father's release."

"And they all live happily ever after," Donal added, jokingly.

"On the contrary," Captain Fortescue answered. "That is just the end of Act One. We can only guess at Act Two, but it might begin with Bingham coming to see Queen Elizabeth and persuading her that Granuaile is a rebel and a pirate, and that she needs to be ruthlessly suppressed. It could end with all of you in the Tower of London or even worse. Points of view are often irreconcilable, and there are times when action is safer than words. That is why preparations are being made for your departure. At the theater I was given a message to drive you straight to the wharf. Here we are now."

As the coach drew up, Captain Fortescue jumped out and led the twins along a gangplank onto the O'Malley flagship, now manned and ready to depart.

Grace and Donal stood on the bridge beside Granuaile, looking back at the dim outline of London as it gradually faded away from them into the darkness of the night. All that they had heard from Captain Fortescue colored their reluctance to leave. They could not shake off a feeling of nostalgia as they thought of the Globe Theatre, which they might never see again.

When Granuaile's vessel sailed triumphantly into O'Malley waters with her son Murrough O'Malley safely on board, her people fired salvos of cannon in welcome from every fortified headland. Church bells rang out from hills and valleys. People left fields and cottages to rush down to the water's edge and wade out to cheer Granuaile as she sailed past, dipping her flag to them in salute.

"Was there ever so happy a day in Connaught?" Grace asked her father gaily, as she waved back to the throngs along the shore.

"Connaught was always happy before Bingham came," her father replied, smiling down at her. "And now it is going to be happy again, for ever and ever."

"No more wars, no more hostages," Grace said, smiling happily.

GENEVIEVE FOSTER

The Marriage of Marie Antoinette

Marie Antoinette was a Hapsburg, the most important royal family in Europe for centuries, and still very important when Marie Antoinette was born in the middle of the eighteenth century. Before she died on the guillotine, the divine right of kings would become an outmoded fashion.

MARIE ANTOINETTE, the little Archduchess of Austria, was a lovable child, with golden hair and blue eyes, a gay smile and a warm heart, but she never would learn her lessons. She wanted only to laugh and play. She would slip away from her French teacher, hide from her reading master, and instead of practicing on her harpsichord she would skip gaily off on her twinkling toes, to dance and play in the sunny courtyard.

One October day when she was seven, little "Toinette" was called in from her play to hear a small musician, just a few

From GEORGE WASHINGTON'S WORLD, by Genevieve Foster.

months younger than she was herself, play the violin and harpsichord. He was starting on a concert tour of Europe with his
father and sister. People spoke of him as the "wonder child,"
but his name was Wolfgang Mozart.

Many days thereafter they spent playing together, the little
Archduchess and the small musician. One day, crossing the polished floor, he slipped and fell, and Marie Antoinette quickly
helped him up.

"You are good," said the small Mozart. "Some day I will marry
you," he added with a smile.

Queen Maria Theresa smiled too, but as he climbed up into
her lap, she thought, "Ah, no, if all goes well it will not be you,
my little one, that my Toinette will marry, but the future King
of France."

And, as she had so eagerly desired, in time all went well. The
formal proposal from Louis XV for the hand of the Princess
came when Marie Antoinette was eleven, and when all the wedding arrangements had been agreed upon to the most minute
detail, the marriage day was set for the spring of 1770, and a
special messenger from France, forty-eight carriages, each drawn
by six horses, and one hundred and seventy-seven bodyguards
were sent to fetch the now precious princess.

As the magnificent coach, specially built for the occasion, covered with glass, painted with scrolls and crowns of gold, carried
her little girl of fourteen out of sight, Marie Theresa, who had
been so eager for that marriage, was sad with the vague premoni-
tion of evil.

"She is so young and heedless," she prayed. "God grant that no
harm befall her."

It was a long journey of six hundred miles between the old
home and the new. Marie Antoinette watched the hours go by
on the small watch her mother had given her, smiling at the
thought of all the joyful hours that would be hers at the gayest
court in Europe, smiling at the thought of how gay and charming
the French prince was sure to be, and smiling out at the dear
good peasants of the villages who gathered in their festal dress
to strew the path with flowers, as she passed.

When they had been traveling nearly a month, the horses

came to a stop in a beautiful wood not far from Paris, where in
the dappled sun and shade stood the coaches of the royal family
who had come that far to meet her. In a twinkling, Marie Antoinette slipped from her seat and hastened over to the King.
In a rustle of silk, she made a deep graceful curtsy, then looked
up with expectant eyes . . . and there was her prince—a great
awkward fellow, staring solemnly down at her with large pale-
blue nearsighted eyes. He kissed her dutifully on both cheeks,
with no change of his expression, then, following her and his royal
grandfather, clambered stolidly back to his seat in the coach and
never ventured so much as a word till they reached their destination. On closer acquaintance Marie Antoinette discovered that
there were only two things that Louis the Dauphin ever wanted
to do—make locks and go hunting. Good days he went hunting,
rainy days he hammered away in his smithy making locks, and his
young bride soon found that she would have to make her own
amusements.

That she found very difficult. Almost everything she wanted to
do seemed to be contrary to some rule of etiquette, or was declared, by her lady-in-waiting, as unbecoming conduct. She
couldn't run and play tag with her husband's young brothers,
she mustn't have a dog, she mustn't ride horseback. She mustn't
do this or that. What then could she do? This is the letter she
wrote her mother:

"I get up at half-past nine or ten o'clock, dress, and say my
morning prayers. Then I have breakfast and go to see my aunts.
At eleven, I go to have my hair dressed. Next comes the levée.
I rouge my cheeks and wash my hands before the assembled company; then the gentlemen withdraw, the ladies remain and I dress
myself in their presences. Now it is time for church. If the King
is at Versailles, I go with him, with my husband and my aunts
to mass. After mass we have our dinner in public, but this is over
by half-past one, for we both eat very quickly. Then . . . I retire
to my room, where I read, write, or work. Needlework, for I am
embroidering the King a coat, which gets forward very slowly,
though I hope that with God's grace it will be finished a few
years from now. At half-past six my husband goes with me to
my aunts. From seven to nine we play cards, at nine o'clock we

have supper. We sit there for the King who usually comes at about quarter to eleven. While waiting, I lie down on a big sofa and go to sleep. That is how I spend my day."

It was a dull life instead of a gay one.

By May, 1773, Marie Antoinette had been in Versailles three years and had never seen Paris. The spiteful old aunts, Adelaide, Sophie, and Victoire (there were only three of them now, instead of four), had seen to it that she was deprived of that pleasure. So at last she plucked up courage to ask the King himself.

"And why not?" said the King, and told her to set the day.

So on the eighth of June, Marie Antoinette and the Dauphin made their first and joyous entry into the city of Paris. The procession of their coaches passed through flower-strewn streets, under flying banners and triumphal arches, among crowds of people who pressed close to the carriage to catch a glimpse of the golden-haired girl who would one day be their queen.

"How beautiful she is!" they exclaimed, "and as kindhearted too. Good times are sure to come again when they are king and queen."

Salutes of welcome were fired from the Bastille, as the procession wound slowly through the cheering throng to the Tuileries, the palace where the kings of France had lived in olden times. There the two young people stepped out on the balcony overlooking the garden.

"*Mon Dieu*, how many many people!" Mary Antoinette gave a little gasp of astonishment as she looked down on the upturned faces.

"Madame," said one of their attendants, "you see before you two hundred thousand persons who have fallen in love with you."

Marie Antoinette wrote Maria Theresa about the thrilling day:

"Last Tuesday," she said, "there was a festival which I shall never forget. We made our entry into Paris. Darling Mother, I do not know how to describe the transports of delight and affection shown us. How fortunate to be in a position where one can gain so much affection at so little cost. Such love is precious . . . I shall never forget it!"

BERNARDINE KIELTY

The
Trial and
Execution of
Marie Antoinette

Marie Antoinette was a poor butterfly queen who was caught in the Reign of Terror. To the poor of France, the Revolution meant liberty. To the rich and royal, it meant disaster and tragedy.

THE DAY of her trial was October 12, 1793. True to her feminine instincts Marie Antoinette tried to look her best for that important occasion. Her short white hair was carefully arranged and to her little cap she added two ribbons from which hung black mourning crepe.

The trial is on record and her answers have come down through the years, simple, dignified, accurate. "Marie Antoinette

From MARIE ANTOINETTE, *by Bernardine Kielty.*

of Austria, thirty-eight years of age, widow of the King of
France . . ." For fifteen hours the tribunal questioned her and
she answered. Nothing was achieved except that she was exhausted. When she asked at the end for a glass of water no one
in all that crowd of people was brave enough to get her one.

Finally the officer of the guards who was assigned to escort her
back to her cell gave her a drink of water. This was a man named
De Busne. On her way to the cell she had a dizzy spell. "I am
exhausted," she told him. "I cannot see. I cannot walk." So he
offered to support her, and she took his arm.

The next day De Busne was arrested and convicted as a coun-
terrevolutionary spy. The revolutionaries were afraid of their
shadows.

At the trial Marie Antoinette was given two defenders, lawyers
called by the government to give a semblance of correct legal
procedure. These men were as decorous as are all trial lawyers to
their client. "How tired you must be!" she said at the end of the
second long day when they had summarized their defense.

Her words of commiseration were heard, and both men, before
her eyes, were arrested.

The jury was unanimous in finding Marie Antoinette guilty
as an enemy of the state. And Fouquier-Tinville, the Public Pros-
ecutor, asked for the death sentence.

When the sentence was read, the judge asked the routine question: had she any objection to make to the application of the
sentence? She shook her head. There was no sound, no gesture,
no tear. She walked from the hall with her head erect, and returned to the Conciergerie where she was put into the cell of
those condemned to death.

The pretty little archduchess, the fun-loving dauphiness, the
butterfly queen, was now a woman. Alone in her cell at the Conciergerie she wrote a letter that only a woman of character and
wisdom would have penned. It was to Élisabeth who had up to
now shared her tragedy. The letter is dated October 16, at half-
past four in the morning:

"It is to you, Sister, that I am writing for the last time. I have just been sentenced to death, but not to a shameful one since this death is shameful only to criminals, whereas I am going to rejoin your brother. Innocent like him, I hope to show the firmness which he showed during his last moments . . . You who in the kindness of your heart sacrificed everything to be with us—in what terrible position am I leaving you! I learned during the trial that my daughter has been separated from you. Alas, poor child, I dare not write to her; she would not receive my letter. I do not even know if this one will reach you. But I send them both my blessing in the hope that some day, when they are older, they will be with you once more and will be able to enjoy your tender care . . . May they both feel that whatever their situation they will never be truly happy except together! Let them take pattern from us! How much consolation our affection brought us in our misfortune! I hope my son never forgets his father's last words: *Let him never try to avenge our death!* . . . I here bid farewell to my aunts and to my brothers and sisters. I had friends. The thought of being separated from them forever and of their distress is among my greatest regrets in dying. Let them know at least that in my last moments I have thought of them. . . . Adieu, my good and affectionate sister. I trust that this letter will reach you. Think of me always. I send you my most heartfelt love, and also to my poor dear children. How heartbreaking it is to leave them forever! Adieu, adieu. I must now devote myself entirely to my spiritual duties. . . ." The letter ended abruptly.

Even the handwriting is strong and firm, not the childish unformed letters of other days. She was indeed a woman.

(This letter never reached Élisabeth. Twenty-one years later it was sold by a man who had saved it to make a profit. Princess Élisabeth was guillotined on May 10 of the next year. What happened to the Dauphin is not certain. Either he perished in the Temple, or he lived out his life elsewhere under another name. No one knows.)

At five in the morning the call to arms was beaten in the forty-eight sections of Paris. By seven all the military forces were out.

Cannon was placed on all the nearby bridges, and a cordon of 30,000 soldiers lined the way from the Conciergerie to the Place de la Révolution.

Masses of people crowded around the entrance to the Conciergerie, and a murmur like the waves of the sea spread out over them when at eleven o'clock the gate opened and the Queen stepped out.

She wore a loose dress with a fichu of white muslin around her neck. On her head was a linen cap, and on her feet were black slippers with high heels. She was tall and thin and straight. She looked a queen.

Louis had been driven to his death in a carriage. But for Marie Antoinette there was only a tumbril—a rough cart with a plank for a seat, pulled by a white horse. The Queen sat with her back to the horse and behind her stood the executioner, Samson, holding her elbows back by a cord.

The cart moved with terrible slowness through the crowds of men and women. They were not all shouting. It is said that many fainted, and many wept at a woman's humiliation.

Marie Antoinette climbed the steps of the scaffold without help. In doing so she stepped without meaning to on the hand of Samson, the executioner. He gave an involuntary cry of pain.

"I beg your pardon, Monsieur," the Queen said, polite from force of habit. She had been badly brought up for the important things in life, well brought up only in the small amenities.

At a quarter past twelve, October 16, Marie Antoinette was guillotined and the once proud head was held high by the executioner for the people to see.

"Long live the Republic!" resounded across Paris.

GRACE HUMPHREY

Catherine the Great

Four and thirty years Catherine ruled as Empress in
Russia (1762–96), for the most part with wisdom and
success. When she died, she was buried in a yellow stucco
building, a combination of fortress and cathedral, in St.
Petersburg. On its walls hung many flags, trophies of her
victories in battle. Priests in red velvet and gold swung
their censers near the marble coffin of the little German
girl from Stettin who became the "Star of the North,"
Catherine the Great.

That title is not given to many persons in history.
Come to think of it, is there any other woman in any
country in the world who is called "the Great"?

THE LITTLE PRINCESS wished they were home again in Stettin.
She did not like visiting, because her mother and her governess
gave her such strict orders. At home she could go out into
the streets and play with other children. They never called her
your Highness, but treated her just as if she were a girl of ten
like themselves.

From THE STORY OF THE CATHERINES, by Grace Humphrey.

Here at the Duke of Holstein's there's nobody to play with except that sickly, ill-tempered little Peter, she thought.

At the end of the corridor she caught a glimpse of the young Prince of Holstein who motioned for her to follow him, but make no noise. They tiptoed down a long passage and turned into a bare room. She saw only a big tub of water.

"Quick, let's make some paper boats," suggested Peter.

The cousins made a fleet and launched it. They stirred the water with sticks to get big waves. They sailed their boats across the Baltic Sea in a storm and were having a splendid time when someone seized Peter by the collar and jerked him away.

"Didn't I tell you," roared an angry voice, "you were not to go near that water again? A soldier's first duty is to obey. Go to your room. No dinner today!"

"Oh, Herr Brummer," the lad begged.

"You heard my commands. Not a word. Go."

The little visitor stared at the tall German.

"Are you afraid of your tutor, Peter?" she asked fearlessly. "You're a simpleton. Send him away."

"So—so." The man bowed stiffly. "Do you tell Prince Peter of Holstein to disobey?"

"I do," the girl said firmly. "At home my tutors——"

"Well, this is not Stettin," interrupted Brummer. "The sooner you go there, the better. You'll find Peter a dull playmate."

"Yes, dull," she agreed as she watched the young prince marched off to punishment, "dull and stupid, and pale and thin and obstinate, and fond of drinking, though he is only eleven. Why, Holstein's the dullest of all the places we visit."

They had relatives everywhere and spent most of their time moving about to one little court after another; for Germany at that time—more than two hundred years ago—was not all one country, but swarmed with little princely and ducal houses. Her father, governor of Stettin, was a field marshal in the army of Frederick the Great, so that he was often away from home fighting. Her mother thought the town dull and hated to live in one wing of the big château, but there was no money to keep up a large establishment. She was ambitious and fond of pleasure and eager for excitement and gossip.

"All this visiting," she would defend herself to her husband, "is for our daughter. We meet all the young princes and so I can pick out a husband for her. I want one who will some day sit on a throne!"

But these boys with their long names and titles were, the girl decided, awkward and stupid—as stupid as Peter, Prince of Holstein, heir to the throne of Sweden, and one of the heirs of the Czar of Russia. She had rather a long name herself—Sophia Augusta Frederika, Princess of Anhalt-Zerbst. But no one today calls her that.

No matter where they happened to be staying the little girl heard over and over talk of Russia, that wild and savage and mysterious land to the east—talk of its great size and unknown strength, talk of its splendor and luxury, of its sudden change from barbarism to Western civilization; stories of the emperor who had not so long before laid siege to Stettin, and of Peter the Great who conquered the Danes and worked as a shipbuilder and built a great city in the north where he could look out on Europe.

Suddenly there came exciting news from Russia. Elizabeth, a daughter of that Peter the Great, had imprisoned the little czar Ivan and seated herself on the throne. A month later she summoned her nephew, the young Prince of Holstein, and with solemn ceremony named him the Grand Duke Peter and proclaimed him as her heir.

A year went by. In the castle of Zerbst the family were celebrating Christmas in the festive German way. A courier dashed up to the door with a letter. The father and mother were talking it over when another courier arrived with a note from Frederick the Great. There was a long discussion. At last they called their daughter in.

"The letter is from Herr Brummer," began the mother.

"Brummer? Oh yes, I remember. He used to be Peter's tutor."

"But he's a tutor no longer. He's Master of the Household of the Grand Duke Peter. He invites me to come at once to the imperial court of Russia—and to bring you with me."

She broke off and turned to her husband.

"Now my dreams and my hopes and my ambitions can come true!"

Not a word did she say about the second letter that told what was back of this invitation—Frederick the Great's plan to make Russia his ally by marrying Peter and Sophia Augusta Frederika. Instead she asked, "How soon can we pack and start? Brummer says we must not delay."

Three dresses, a dozen chemises, stockings and twelve handkerchiefs were all the daughter had to pack for this momentous journey. And the Empress, rumor said, had fifteen thousand silk dresses and five thousand pairs of shoes!

What a journey the two women had! It was the dead of winter, so bitterly cold they had to wear masks to protect their faces. Their four heavy coaches—for they took with them a maid of honor, an officer, a cook, and half a dozen servants plus all their luggage—had six horses apiece, not for show but to pull them through the mud.

Frederick the Great had sent orders ahead to the keepers of the posting-houses to have everything ready for the travelers. But there were no fires and they had to take refuge in the landlord's room. Husband and wife, children, chickens, watchdog, guests—all slept pell-mell in cradles, beds, mattresses behind the stove.

The scene changed when they reached the frontier of Russia. Regiments of soldiers appeared to escort them, then the vice-governor in a state chariot. As they drove to the castle cannon fired salutes. Drums were beating in the court. Gorgeous uniforms, gowns of velvet and silk and gold—bows to the floor, kissing of hands—hundreds of candles burning in the magnificent rooms. Were they dreaming? Was all this for them?

Their journey across Russia was as splendid as a fairy tale. They stopped for several days in St. Petersburg to make sure, as the Empress put it, that their toilettes conformed to the fashions of her land—a tactful way of filling their wardrobes. They lived in the famous Winter Palace and found it very different from the frugal, simple courts of little German duchies.

Someone pointed out to them the barracks from which Elizabeth started out to seize the throne. They saw parading down the broad avenue along the Neva the grenadiers of the very regiment that had marched with her that winter night—a sight the young girl did not forget.

With far more than three dresses and a dozen chemises the Princess of Anhalt-Zerbst and her mother went on to Moscow where the court then was. Majordomos and equerries and soldiers, cooks and butlers and lackeys and maids, guards and stableboys made up their escort. They rode in the imperial sledge, a marvelous vehicle invented by Peter the Great. It was of scarlet wood trimmed with gold and lined with sable; long enough to lie down in comfort—indeed it had a feather bed with silken cushions and furred covers, with red curtains embroidered in gold.

Day and night they drove on and on to reach Moscow by the Grand Duke's birthday. For the last relay their sledge had sixteen horses and they made fifty miles without a stop. Did the ambitious, scheming mother remember the dull lad Peter had been, and wonder if he had improved, or did she think only of what he would soon give her daughter, a seat beside him on the throne of Russia? The drivers cracked their whips and with a flourish pulled up before the wooden palace in Moscow.

Behind a double row of courtiers the Empress was waiting impatiently to receive her guests. More impatient still, Peter dashed into their room to greet them before they had time to take off their furs.

Coached by Herr Brummer, they bowed before the Empress and kissed her hand. That little act of humility won her over.

"The marriage is a settled thing," the mother wrote shortly to her husband.

No one asked her daughter if she wished to marry the Grand Duke Peter. No one argued that they were cousins and so this step would be unwise. No one questioned whether or not any bride could be happy with such a husband. Had it not been planned by Frederick the Great and the Empress? Then say no more, it is settled.

"There's one thing I must do," the young German princess announced to herself, "if I'm ever to amount to anything in Russia —I must make myself over and become a Russian. Peter's never given it a thought, I'm sure. But I can see how the courtiers dislike his German manners and his Holstein dialect. I'll start lessons in Russian at once."

A wise decision for a girl of fifteen to make: she had admirable good sense and soundness of judgment, and she was quick to size up a new situation. Later on, these qualities stood her in good stead. Perhaps they were the foundation of her genius.

She used to get up at night to repeat the lessons set her by her Russian master. It was very cold. Barefoot she walked up and down, up and down, saying the strange, unfamiliar words aloud— barefoot because the cold helped her to keep awake. She took a chill, grew rapidly worse, and came down with pneumonia.

"Her life is in danger," said the doctors. "There is only one remedy—bloodletting."

"No, no," argued the frightened mother. "You shall not! You shall not!"

"We will ask the Empress."

"Yes—if it will save her life," ordered Elizabeth.

As the doctors began their work the poor girl fainted. When she was herself again she found the arms of the Empress about her. To console her for the prick of the lancet she was given a diamond necklace and earrings.

"Take them, child," whispered her mother. "They're worth twenty thousand rubles."

Presents or not, pneumonia was a serious matter. Day after day the girl was bled—sixteen times in less than a month—once, four times in twenty-four hours.

"It is the only remedy," insisted the doctors.

At last her youth and robust health won the victory over the disease and over the treatment for it. While she was convalescing she found herself with new friends. Her mother had argued with the doctors, scolded the attendants, fussed over her daughter, disputed with the Grand Duke and the Empress till every one disliked her. The patient won all hearts.

Her illness made the Russians love her, for it was noised abroad how she came by it. They pictured her barefoot, pacing her room, trying to master the difficult sounds in order to become a thorough Russian.

"She will be our Grand Duchess," they boasted.

They heard too a second story—how at the crisis the mother wished to summon a Lutheran pastor.

"No," the sick girl replied, "why? Send for——" and she named the Russian priest who had charge of Peter's religious education.

"She'll be Russian to the very core," said the people delightedly. "Her position in our country is assured."

So it came about that, one June morning, she was formally received into the Russian Church. The royal chapel was crowded. Sophia Augusta Frederika wore a red dress laced with silver, and a simple white ribbon about her unpowdered hair. Without hesitating, without a mistake she recited the long creed—in Russian. The priest gave her a new name—Catherina Alexiewna.

"The Catherine is simply added to Sophia as we do at confirmation," her mother explained to the strict Lutherans of her family. "And that long, unpronounceable name means 'the daughter of Augustus'—there isn't any word for it in Russian."

Her old names were lost from that time forth. Now, to all the world she was Catherine.

The next day came the formal betrothal in the cathedral, followed by a reception, a state dinner at two in the afternoon, a gala supper and ball until two in the morning. For the first time Catherine was officially named the Grand Duchess. For the first time she sat upon a throne.

"If I am to be a Russian," she said to herself, "I must see more of this great country."

The opportunity came when the court went on a pilgrimage to Kiev. As a child she'd seen only petty duchies and little kingdoms. Now she journeyed five hundred miles without leaving the dominions of the Empress. On every side she saw grandeur and luxury and power—evidently without limit. The idea fascinated her.

She saw too for the first time the common people of Russia. They were bowed down in misery and bondage. They shivered with cold and hunger in their smoky hovels. Sordid they were, savage, unhappy. Was this the result when great power was abused? What might be done by a ruler of liberal ideas?

"Russia is a land of extremes"—she described it to herself—"of lavish wealth and utter poverty—of splendor and barbarism—of ease and misery. But its future—that has no limit. Why should not its resources be developed until Russia is the most powerful and the most splendid state in Europe?"

Peter came down with the measles, then with smallpox, and the wedding had to be put off more than once. Marvelous preparations were made. Court officials were sent to France to get the details of the Dauphin's recent wedding, and to Dresden where the King's son had just been married. They brought back pages and pages of descriptions of court etiquette, illustrations and measurements for this and for that.

"We will surpass Versailles!" announced the Empress.

As soon as the ice on the Neva broke up, ships came in laden with wondrous cargoes—carriages, fabrics, liveries, English cloth woven with large flowers of gold and silver. A complete trousseau was planned for the bride—linen and lace and dresses and jewels.

In the middle of August, heralds in armor rode to different parts of St. Petersburg and with beating of drums announced to the people the wedding of their Grand Duke and Grand Duchess on the twenty-first of that month. Around the Kazan cathedral platforms were built, hung with red velvet. Tables were set up in the streets for the banquets to the people, fountains which were to flow with wine.

The booming of guns and the chiming of church bells wakened all the city on the day of the wedding. Troops assembled and lined the streets from the Winter Palace to the cathedral.

At ten o'clock the procession started. The fair-haired, dark-eyed bride was bewitchingly beautiful. Her dress was shot with silver. The skirt halfway up was richly embroidered in gold. Her hair was not powdered. She wore a small coronet of diamonds which the Empress herself placed on her head.

From the palace gates came the long line of a hundred and twenty court equipages, each with footmen and pages and runners. It was broken here and there by mounted escorts of dragoons and hussars and guards. Drums and trumpets sounded.

Then came the Grand Master of Ceremonies in an open carriage with his mace of office. Next the Lord High Chamberlain attended by a great number of officers on horseback.

"Here they are! Here she comes!" people shouted, and broke into cheering. The imperial chariot was drawn by eight horses led by grooms. In it sat the Empress with Peter and Catherine.

"The procession was the finest ever known in this country," said the British ambassador in his official report of the wedding, "and infinitely surpassed anything I've ever seen."

From the Winter Palace along the Neva to the cathedral was not a great distance, but the bridal party did not arrive until one o'clock. The ceremony was carried out with all the gorgeous ritual of the Russian Church. It lasted until after four and then the long procession returned to the palace.

For ten days the festivities went on—the gayest ten days ever known in Europe. There were balls and masquerades, state banquets and dinners and suppers, Italian operas and French plays, illuminations and splendid fireworks. The wealth of Crœsus seemed showered on this bride of sixteen.

Then her mother was packed off to Stettin, and Catherine was left alone to fight her own battles. The court had a rich setting with all the luxury and pomp of the sovereigns of western Europe. The palaces had suite after suite of showy rooms with inlaid floors and mirrored walls. The courtiers were dressed in silks and velvets, laced with gold, starred with diamonds. Yet among all the men who kissed her hand, the women who paid her compliments, Catherine had not one friend.

The Empress was jealous and suspicious. She had always one spy in the group of attendants on the Grand Duchess. Every word, every act was promptly reported. The girl's letters to her mother were opened and read, and soon they were forbidden. When word came of her father's death she cried for several days.

"Her Majesty orders you to leave off grieving," commanded one of the ladies-in-waiting. "A week of mourning is quite enough. Your father was not a king, remember."

A monotonous, boresome time Catherine had, month after month, year after year. They moved from one palace to another. The same court functions went on, the same dull parties.

And her husband? Without Herr Brummer's guiding hand Peter had gone from worse to worst. If she disliked him as a boy, she must have despised him as a man. He was neither a soldier nor a gentleman, for he was cowardly and violent and braggart. He had no education, but amused himself with dolls and puppets. He would sit up in bed and play with his theater of marionettes for hours at a time. He had whole regiments of toy soldiers.

"What are you doing with that rat?" Catherine asked one day when she found him busily engaged with a poor little creature he had trapped.

"Holding a court-martial. He ate one of my paste sentinels, and we're going to hang him."

In the alcove of their bedroom behind a thin partition of boards Peter kept a pack of five or six hounds. By day they barked, by night they cried piercingly when their master drilled and whipped them. If they chanced to be quiet he would seize his violin, on which he could not play, and walk up and down making a great noise to rouse them.

What happiness could she have with such a husband? Peter was extravagant and thoughtless. He had guardroom manners and often guardroom language. The taste for drink that he'd had as a boy conquered him, now that he was older. Day after day he was drunk. His favorites must be men and women who would drink and carouse with him.

While he wasted his life, his bride hunted for some solace. He neglected her for weeks at a time. Public receptions and balls and masquerades did not wholly fill the long dull days.

Fortunately she was allowed books. Alone and deserted, she would often read the whole day through. French books, German books, Russian books—romances and philosophy, the history of country after country she read and studied. She had a good mind, trained and stimulated by the restraint in which she lived. Little by little her intellectual powers began to show.

Ambassadors and chancellors who had any dealings with her were struck by her ability, the common sense of her remarks, the shrewdness of her outlook on the world. They saw her charm and cleverness. They noticed how alert she was, how vivacious, how tactful.

"She's like a Cinderella on the steps of a throne," said one.

"Yes. When Peter is czar, who will be the real ruler? He consults her now in every serious matter. She has genuine capacity for the business of state. We had best set to work to win her friendship."

And they did. Before this Grand Duchess, barely out of her teens, opened a new horizon that dazzled her eyes and tempted her ambition—politics. A fascinating game where Poland and England and Prussia and France and Austria plotted and intrigued and conspired, all of them anxious to have Russia as an ally. This was a game worth playing!

What else remained to her besides ambition? Her husband, brutal and coarse and worthless, cared nothing for her. Her baby Paul was taken away and brought up by the Empress; she could see him now and then at long intervals. But to rule over this land of Russia, to carve out her own fame and a greater fame for her empire—why, there was no limit to her ambition!

Elizabeth was old and often ill. What would come with her death—revolution? Peter as czar? Or the baby Paul? Perhaps with Catherine as regent? All Europe was interested in the answer to these questions.

Yet nothing startling occurred when the Empress died at the end of 1761. The Grand Duke was quietly proclaimed as Peter III. Not a word was said of his wife and son.

On the throne of Peter the Great sat now Peter the Impossible. In his drunken, pig-headed, insolent way he made two enemies. The first was the army. He replaced the royal guards with a regiment from Holstein. He changed their comfortable, loose-fitting uniforms for the tight, irksome Prussian dress. He introduced the iron discipline of Frederick the Great and made the soldiers whom Elizabeth had pampered and spoiled drill in the open every day, no matter what the weather.

His second enemy was Catherine. He sought out ways to humiliate her and show his contempt. Because she was fond of fruit he gave orders none should be served at table. At a state dinner where the four hundred guests included the foreign ministers and the highest dignitaries of the realm he openly insulted her.

"The health of the imperial family!" someone proposed a toast.

Scarcely had Catherine set down her glass when Peter sent his aide to ask why she did not rise to drink the toast.

"I did not think it necessary," she replied. "The imperial family is the Emperor, myself and our son. It was not right for me to drink my own health standing."

"Tell her she is a fool!" was his hasty order. "She ought to know my uncles in Holstein are a part of the imperial family."

Then, as if he feared the aide would not carry his message exactly, he leaned across the table and shouted at the top of his voice so that everyone could hear, addressing the word without a doubt to his wife:

"*Doura! Doura!*" (Fool! Fool!)

Poor Catherine!

In a roundabout way she learned Peter's plans to divorce her and shut her up in a convent, imprison the boy Paul, and then marry his favorite. Plotting began on her side. A little group of loyal friends won over four regiments of the royal guards who were already bitter against the Emperor. They would work very slowly and in some months or a year's time be ready to dethrone him.

In July, fate ordered otherwise. Thinking that his colonel was in the secret, a young captain asked, "When do we march against the Czar?" and was promptly arrested. Word of this reached Catherine's friends in the middle of the night. There was a hurried discussion. What should be done? One of them, young Orlof, ordered a coach and at top speed drove out to the château some twenty miles from St. Petersburg where the Empress was staying.

"It's time to get up!" he cried as he wakened her at five o'clock. "Everything's ready for the proclamation."

She sleepily asked him to explain and heard his story. Her keen, alert mind began to plan and scheme. Very hurriedly she dressed and with one of her maids took her place in the coach that waited at the garden gate. Orlof mounted in front with the driver and off they set at a gallop. Soon they met the French hairdresser, on his way to wait upon Catherine, and took him along with them.

One thing had been forgotten—relays of horses. The poor creatures harnessed to the coach were worn out long before the return trip was over. By good fortune they met on the highroad a peasant's cart, borrowed its team, and so won the race against time.

The clocks were striking seven when they pulled up in front of the barracks. A strange party it was—the wife of the Emperor, a maid, a hairdresser, an officer of the guards. They found only a dozen men lounging about. Nothing was ready.

"Beat the drums!" ordered Orlof.

Half asleep the soldiers came tumbling out of the building. Half dressed they fell into line. At the word of command they shouted, "Long live the Empress!" just as those regiments had called out that phrase a few years before when Elizabeth seized the throne.

"Fetch a priest," Catherine commanded, "and be quick!"

Two of the men found a chaplain and dragged him in. He raised the cross and mumbled out a form of oath. When the order was given, all the soldiers bowed down. The Empress was proclaimed sole and absolute sovereign of Russia. Not a word of Paul who was Peter's rightful heir. A woman, a foreigner, a stranger to the imperial blood was seated on the throne. Without the loss of a life the new reign was established.

In the Kazan cathedral Catherine stood to receive the oaths of loyalty from her subjects. Great crowds flocked into the building —the senate, the heads of the church, the chancellor with little Paul in his nightcap. The soldiers were mad with joy and wept and shouted.

In front of the Winter Palace the Empress reviewed the troops. She was on horseback, dressed in the uniform of the guards. One of the officers noticed that her hat had no plume. In a flash he rode out of the line, bowed low over his saddle, and taking his own plume from his helmet fastened it to hers.

"Who is that?" she asked someone near her.

"One of the minor nobles, Potemkin."

She remembered the name as the guards shouted again and again, "Long live our Empress!"

And what of Peter III all this time? On the day of the revolution he was to dine at his wife's château with a group of his friends. They arrived in the middle of the afternoon and found the place deserted. They called and at last were answered by a few servants overcome with terror.

"Where is her Majesty?"

"Gone!"

"Where? Where?"

No one could answer.

A peasant came up with a note. Peter tore it open. His valet sent word that the Empress had been proclaimed at St. Petersburg as sole ruler of Russia. He could not believe it. Like a madman he rushed through the empty rooms, hunted in the closets and in all the corners, looked under the beds, dashed into the garden, calling over and over, "Catherine! Catherine!"

An hour later he remembered that he was a soldier, put on his uniform, and sent for his Holstein regiment.

"Go to Kronstadt at once, sire," urged his field marshal, "and seize that fortress."

As if it were a pleasure party, Peter and the seventeen ladies who had come for dinner set out on a yacht. It was midnight when they arrived.

"Who goes there?" called a sentinel on the ramparts.

"The Emperor."

"We have no emperor any longer."

"But it is *I*. Don't you know me?"

"Pass away there!"

The women shrieked. Trembling, Peter hid in the hold and ordered the yacht to go back. He could hear the garrison cheering for Catherine.

Almost at that hour twenty thousand soldiers marched out from St. Petersburg. They had thrown off the hated Prussian uniform and gaily donned their old Russian garb. At their head rode the Empress in the dress of a colonel of the royal guards. Her cap had a band of sable and a crown of oak leaves. Her long hair floated in the wind.

All night they marched. In the morning they met a messenger with a white flag.

"A note from the Emperor," said the prince who presented it with a deep bow.

"Read it," Catherine ordered. "He offers to divide the power with me? There is no answer."

An hour later she received his abdication. Thus Peter III gave up the throne of Peter the Great. Thus in the summer of 1762 Catherine II came into power—a farseeing statesman, a brilliant commander, fearless, masterful, charming, energetic.

Said Frederick the Great, "Peter allowed himself to be deposed like a whipped child that is sent to bed."

Four days later he was found dead in his room. Was he poisoned? Murdered? By Catherine's order? With her knowledge perhaps, and her approval? No one is sure. All we can say certainly is that nobody was tried for his death.

Thus began the long reign that won her the name of Catherine the Great.

Though Peter had ruled for some months, he had never been crowned. Catherine determined that her coronation should fulfill every Russian tradition. She knew how much that would please the people, how it would appeal to their imagination.

All Moscow turned out to welcome her when she arrived there in September. Stands were erected along the main streets and covered with gay carpets. The church bells pealed their welcome.

In the cathedral she herself placed the purple on her shoulders and put the crown on her head, after the manner of the czars. During the long service she stood on the throne, the scepter in her right hand, the orb in her left. Cannon boomed forth the announcement of the coronation. The crowds cheered enthusiastically and scrambled for the silver coins thrown out.

The festivities went on for a week. Catherine received the nobles, the gentry, officers, people of every rank. The street fountains ran with wine. Oxen were roasted in the open to serve the public banqueting tables.

Even before her coronation Catherine took up energetically the many problems of the government. Her ambitions for Russia were boundless. Peter the Great had left his task unfinished. If Russia was to hold the place he had given her among the nations of Europe, there was much to be accomplished. The mere list seemed more than one woman could do.

She made a new code of laws. She studied and compared the laws of other countries and with her own hand wrote out minute instructions—enough to fill a whole book—to direct the six hundred deputies summoned for this special work. When the discussions were ended she gave to each man a gold medal stamped with her picture and the words, "For the happiness of each and all—December, 1766." She sent copies of these laws to all the sovereigns of Europe.

Said one of them when he had looked through the book, "More than once in history women have obtained a deserved fame as rulers—Semiramis for conquest, Elizabeth for political wisdom, Maria Theresa for firmness of character. To Catherine alone we give the title of legislator and well she deserves that glory."

But new laws were not enough to remedy all the injustice and the abuses that existed in Russia.

"I find with sorrow," she wrote in one of her decrees, "that corruption is everywhere. If a man has to defend himself it is with money. If he wishes to accuse his neighbor falsely, he can by money carry out his wicked design. All this I will abolish."

Her remedy was to add to the number of courts and judges until she had over three hundred instead of fifty, and to administer the local government in smaller districts. To the end of her reign she carried on a campaign against bribery.

When she came to the throne she found the finances in a muddle. The army had not been paid for eight months. The treasury was empty, with an enormous debt. Bread was double in price. Elizabeth and Peter had hoarded as much money as they could, separating their funds from the nation's.

"I myself," was Catherine's announcement to the senate when five days after the revolution it met to discuss Russia's money troubles, "I myself belong to the state and everything I have is its property. In future no distinction shall be made between my personal interests and those of our country."

She started a state bank, abolished the farming out of taxes, and doubled the revenues of the empire. She decreed religious toleration. She encouraged trade and started factories. She built canals and forts, hospitals and schools—elementary schools in every city, schools to train teachers, military and naval schools, a school of engineering, of commerce. She sent to Italy and Germany, to Oxford for instructors. The best of all the classics she had translated into Russian. She wrote herself—plays and stories, poems and history. The Russian theater owes its beginnings to her.

St. Petersburg, the city in the north that was laid out in a marsh, she planned to make a place of beauty. She adorned it with splendid palaces, fine bridges over the Neva, many public buildings. She put up an imposing monument to Peter the Great. She found it a village of hovels and left it a city of brick and marble.

For her own pleasure she built the Hermitage, connecting it with the Winter Palace by a long passage. It was museum, art gallery, library and theater all in one. She filled its rooms with treasures from the whole of Europe—paintings and prints, rare books, engraved gems, collections of natural history, Voltaire's library.

"Leave your rank outside," read the first of the ten rules she posted at the entrance, "along with your hat and your sword."

Without any of the ceremony of the court Catherine met at the Hermitage the gifted men and women attracted to St. Petersburg—poet and playwright, singer and violinist and harpist, sculptor and portrait painter, historian and scientist. They gave concerts and operas, French plays, Russian comedies. They had real conversation—a Paris salon on the banks of the Neva. In Russia these years are still called "Catherine's time," much as we say "an Elizabethan period" to describe a reign when arts and letters flourished.

"Happy the writer," exclaimed Voltaire, "who a century hence shall tell the history of Catherine II!"

NANCY BARNES

Carlota, American Empress

Carlota was a fairytale princess, tall and regal, gay and charming. Her father was Leopold, King of the Belgians, sometimes called "the matchmaker of Europe." Had he not married off a Coburg boy—Albert—to cousin Vicky and the throne of England? And was not his own daughter twice as handsome as Victoria, thrice as regal, and intelligent, too? When she was married to Prince Charming, did they not deserve the very best that royalty had to offer? The answer lies in Carlota's dream and Maximilian's tragic destiny.

"YES, A PRIG," repeated Leopold teasingly. "That's what you'll grow into, if you don't take care."

Young Princess Charlotte of Belgium turned on her brother impatiently. "But don't you see, I have to be intelligent! Since I shan't ever be beautiful, I've got to be frightfully clever. It's the only thing."

From CARLOTA, AMERICAN EMPRESS, by Nancy Barnes.

She was not being wistful. She was simply stating facts. But Leopold, staring at her with the appraising eye of a precocious young man, surprised her.

"I wouldn't be too sure about that," he remarked, with kindness rather unusual in a critical brother. "About the beauty, I mean. You're really not so bad, you know. No, not bad at all," he added thoughtfully.

Charlotte sniffed. "Beauty? Me! With red hair and green eyes!" She puffed out her cheeks in an exaggerated caricature of their somewhat pompous father. "Preposterous, my boy! Pre-e— posterous!"

Leopold grinned. "Your hair isn't red anymore. It's—auburn. And getting darker all the time. And your eyes . . . well, they're rather amazing, you know. Those great black pupils, and then that almost transparent green rim around them. They're like a heron's eyes." He shivered. "Creepy, rather," he added.

But as Charlotte's face fell, he hastened to comfort her. "Oh, not nasty-creepy. Just strange. Rather stunning I expect, really. And you're going to be tall, I think. A princess should always be tall."

Charlotte stared into her mirror for many minutes after her brother had gone. She was twelve and she had never looked at herself, really seeing herself, this way before. She had only looked to wash her face, or to see if her braids were smooth.

"A princess should always be tall," she repeated aloud, eyeing her lanky legs and arms dubiously. Then she drew herself up, and stared at her reflection haughtily. "*A regal girl, and slim,*" she whispered, quoting one of her favorite fairytales.

"When Victoria was my age, she was dumpy," Charlotte remarked aloud, with satisfaction.

As far back as she could remember, her cousin, Victoria of England, had always been held up as an example to her. Victoria is this—Victoria is that—until Charlotte was almost sick of her cousin's name. Her father, King Leopold of Belgium, was forever dragging it in. "A princess must always carry herself royally— like Victoria."

From the days when Charlotte and her two brothers had been taken out to walk in the public park in Brussels, there had always been the thought that she must act like a princess. She was the daughter of Leopold, first King of the new small kingdom of Belgium. Her mother was Marie Louise, the queen. Furthermore, her mother's father was Louis Philippe, King of France. So Charlotte was doubly royal.

"A princess must always carry herself royally," Papa used to say. Mama said, "A princess must be good." But Mama was like that. She was very religious. And if ever small Charlotte so far forgot herself as to skip or jump, or show any other sign of excitement or exuberance, then Papa or her governess was sure to remind her by that warning she had learned thoroughly to detest: *"Doucement! Doucement!"*

It was better for Leopold and Eugene, her brothers. They were boys, and though even they were never allowed to run and play and shout noisily, they could at least amuse themselves with the games they made up as they walked together. Charlotte used to watch them as they marched ahead with their tutor, their shoulders erect, their steps snapping in unison, playing soldiers.

"Girls are no good for soldiers," they always told her. "Girls are for sewing and embroidery. And for taking care of the children."

Rebellion always mounted in Charlotte when she heard that. "When I'm grown up I'll do everything better than they do. I'll—I'll . . ."

It was natural that she should dream much of marriage. Advantageous marriages were rather a specialty of Papa's. "The matchmaker of Europe," some wit had called him. He had never quite recovered from his success, years before, in marrying a Coburg boy to Cousin Vicky and the throne of England. And he had maneuvered another Coburg to the throne of Portugal, as consort.

And now Charlotte herself was sixteen and nothing—*nothing*—was happening. True, she could go to balls now. Four times a year Papa gave a great ball, and Charlotte, stiff with brocade, and even with a train, could attend.

"But I can only dance with royalty," she pouted to her brother. "And, oh, Leopold, royalty's so scarce! And then Papa only allows me to dance the promenade dances. If only I could waltz . . ."

"Waltzing's not so much," Leopold told her airily, from his vantage point as a man of the world. "It gets awfully dull, really!"

That, Charlotte could not believe. To whirl and dip and glide, in the arms of some handsome prince . . . She sat, with a lovely smile, and watched the court ladies dance with whom they pleased, while her dreams whirled inside her pretty head.

Johann Strauss was writing such beautiful music. The waltz, though not new in the great world, was still shocking many people. Papa had forbidden Charlotte ever to dance in a man's arms like that. But at the last ball something must have softened him. "Perhaps," thought Charlotte, "he's remembering when he was the handsomest young man in Europe!" At any rate, he did at last consent for her to waltz.

"But only with your brothers, Charlotte! Now hear me!"

But Leopold could be charming, and this night he was, as they finished a breathless waltz together. "You're really a beauty, Lotta," he said approvingly. "And that blue becomes you. You should always wear it." He handed her to her seat and swept her a fine bow. "I'm proud of my lovely sister," he said.

Charlotte could scarcely believe her ears. "Beautiful?" It couldn't be true. And yet, somewhere deep inside her the word clicked into place with the finality of foreknowledge, as if, now that it had happened, she had always known. She'd be grown up and then she'd be beautiful and then . . . then life would begin.

"Did you know my famous brother-in-law is to pay us a visit?" Leopold said, as he turned to go. That was just like a brother, to pretend this was a matter of no importance! Charlotte was on her feet, her hand grasping his sleeve, regardless of her usually almost austere dignity.

"Leopold! Not Franz Joseph?" she cried.

"*Not* Franz Joseph," Leopold agreed, grinning down at her. "Maximilian, my dear. Max, the beau ideal of Europe." He eyed his sister's flushed cheeks and shining eyes with amusement.

"Oh, Leopold! Not really!"

"Really! I'm to start to the coast to meet him tomorrow. And if I know my mother-in-law—and alas I do—Max is wife-hunting, Charlotte. So it's as well you've learned to waltz. We'll have another turn later," he ended kindly. "Max is a much traveled young man. He'll expect perfection in any girl."

Charlotte gasped. "Oh, Leopold! As if Papa would let me waltz with anyone but the family. He never would. D-do you think he would?" Excitement made her stutter.

Leopold laughed. "I think he might," he said dryly. "Oh yes, under the circumstances, Charlotte, I really think he might."

It was a dazzled girl who laid her whirling head on her pillow that night. One of the handsomest young men in Europe coming to stay! At Laeken, where nothing ever happened!

Max arrived, and he was all that Charlotte had dreamed he might be. All and more. The whiskers were more. He was tall and she had dreamed of a tall lover. He had sea-blue eyes and lovely, waving gold hair. He was exactly like the fairy prince of any young girl's dream . . . except for the whiskers.

Parted in the center, those whiskers cascaded off into twin sections, twisted to points. "That's to hide the Habsburg jaw," Charlotte thought wisely. "Or . . . can it be that he has a weak chin?" She wondered.

Blushing, she wondered too if she could ever learn to endure those luxuriant golden-red whiskers brushing her cheek when he kissed her. "For, of course, he'd want to kiss me," she sighed. "Men are like that."

The little Belgian court was agog. The old palace at Laeken fairly trembled with gaiety. Charlotte was everywhere, overseeing, giving orders, receiving guests, helping her father entertain Maximilian.

The young man missed none of this capability. "She rules the court as smoothly as if she were sixty," he wrote home in one of those chatty travel letters at which he excelled. And, he told himself, thank heaven she was beautiful. He had almost given up expecting that in a princess.

When they met, he had seen a regal girl, tall, slim, commanding. He found her seriousness sweet. A princess should be serious,
conscious of her dignity and of the high purposes of life. Max
was exacting about dignity. He had written his brother Franzi
some very critical letters about the loose manners of the French
court of Napoleon III. Charlotte was conscious enough of her
royal blood to please even him.

It was December before Max finally gave his critical family the
satisfaction of knowing that his mind was made up to marry. A
secret messenger was at once dispatched to ask Leopold for Charlotte in marriage.

Charlotte was almost too wild with joy. "You must not over-
excite yourself so," Leopold had to warn her. "Softly, softly, my
child. Control is especially necessary for you."

But he had little time for admonitions. His triumph was complete now. Or almost. Those Habsburgs had seen fit to keep him
on tenterhooks over Charlotte, had they? Well, Leopold knew
a trick worth two of that. He smiled to himself when, after he
had given his consent to the marriage, the impetuous Maximilian
sent immediate announcement of his wedding to every court in
Europe.

Only then, when it was too late for the Habsburgs to withdraw
without looking ridiculous, Leopold announced his terms. He
did not, he said, believe in dowries. He was, too, a poor man.
He would give Charlotte a splendid wedding at Saint Gudule.
She would have her mother's jewels. The Belgian Chambers had
voted the girl a small sum of money. That would be all.

Franz Joseph knew as well as did Leopold that Austria could
not retreat without looking foolish. After frowning deliberation,
he appointed Maximilian viceroy over the upper Italian province
of Lombardy and Venetia. Safe in Italy and with a demanding
young beauty for a wife, Max would, he told himself, be too busy
to be a nuisance in Vienna.

Charlotte heard of the appointment with mixed feelings. It
would be splendid to have a palace and a kingdom of her own to
rule. "It's not a crown," she thought sadly. "Max would make

such a superb figure of a king. Why, only the Romanoffs are taller. And with me to—to prod him——"

But Italy would be lovely and warm. She would make the Italians love them both. "It's a start," she thought, as any young wife might think. "Max is young. I'll make them find something more suitable for us yet."

They were married at Brussels on July 27, 1857, and departed at once for Milan. Charlotte was a sweet and charming wife, Max found. He vowed silently but with romantic fervor that he would protect and cherish her always. He never did notice when this chosen role of his slid from him to be taken up by Charlotte.

They were to be very happy in Milan. They settled there for their honeymoon, two pleasant, rather spoiled youngsters, so ordinary as to be just like thousands of other young married couples who hope to be happy and to get ahead.

They were not very bright perhaps. Neither of them ever had any slightest sense of reality. Neither of them had ever been trained to look much beneath the surface, to weigh motives or to suspect that the world did not owe them a perfectly splendid life.

Charlotte changed her name to the Italian form, Carlotta, and they were very happy, at first, in their honeymoon kingdom. But after two years, the Austrians lost the Italian provinces, and Max and Carlotta lost their titles and their palace. Where should they go now?

Max would have been content to retire to Miramar, the handsome limestone palace he had been building on the shores of the Adriatic, not far from Trieste.

But not Carlotta. For one of her imperious nature, the situation was torture. Her ambition was too great to permit her handsome husband to retire from the world. And she, after all, was not yet twenty. There must be a crown somewhere for Max.

Actually, Max was far from being forgotten. In the private apartments of a beautiful and ambitious woman in Paris, long secret sessions were going on. A small dark man with great power was agreeing, reluctantly, that Max might—just possibly—be suitable for the high position they were discussing.

The beautiful ambitious woman was the Empress Eugénie of France. The small dark man was Napoleon III, Emperor of France. They were talking about sponsoring a monarchy in Mexico.

Eugénie explained glibly. She had been well coached by Mexican exiles. Civil war had been going on in Mexico for three years, and the disgruntled exiles flocked to the French court.

"What better task could you undertake than the establishment of our beloved Church in this poor bandit-ridden country?" Eugénie asked her husband. Later, she suggested Maximilian's name. The Mexicans would like a Bourbon prince, she had heard.

"He'd never accept," Napoleon objected. "Why should he?"

But in the end, the offer was made and accepted. England and Spain joined France with some vague promises of support, financial and military. Maximilian was encouraged to believe that he would be greeted with a great popular uprising in his favor. He wanted to believe this, and so did Carlotta, who changed her name again to Carlota, the Spanish form of Charlotte.

Warning voices reached Maximilian from time to time. But he was too excited to listen. Neither he nor Carlota heeded the warnings from their royal relatives that Mexico might not welcome them, or that the offers of support might fade.

Maximilian saw himself as the descendant of Spanish royalty, at last bringing peace and happiness to a horde of grateful dusky subjects, who would bless his name and hand it down in history as that of a great liberator. Carlota saw herself as a fitting consort to this bright and shining figure. Both of them continued to live in a rosy haze of wishful thinking even after they arrived in Mexico.

Neither Max nor Carlota was prepared for what actually happened. They found no royal welcome in Mexico. The rebels under Juárez continued their guerrilla warfare. The young couple redecorated the palace of Chapultepac lavishly, but it was an empty court.

Everything they did went wrong. Napoleon withdrew his troops and canceled his offers of support. The United States demanded that all French troops be removed from Mexico. A new war broke out in Europe. Maximilian would have to save himself, if he could.

Maximilian realized sooner than Carlota how hopeless the whole Mexican affair had become. He could no longer delude himself with wishful thinking. Maximilian smiled sadly as he tried to explain to Carlota that he had failed. He would have to return to Europe, to admit to Napoleon, and to his proud brother Franz Joseph, that he was not wanted in Mexico.

"What else can we do?" he said to Carlota, stroking her dark hair back from her forehead. "We have almost no army. We have no money. We have no friends or support in Europe now. I shall announce my abdication tomorrow."

His spirits rose at once. It was the first clean-cut decision he had been able to make for months. And it was one action he could take, by himself, without the help of anyone else.

"I shall abdicate," he repeated, almost gaily.

Carlota stared at him as if stunned. Her—their—dream world was in ruins about them and Max could be gay! The Coburgs were fighters. All the ambition, the tough stubbornness she had from old Leopold rose in a wave, engulfing her.

Give up a crown? Give up authority and territory? Give up her dream of educating the Indians, healing the sick, seeing her hospitals spread and grow and do good? Give up the charities she had begun and let the Mexicans, so grateful, so quiet and good when she walked among them—let the Mexicans sink back into poverty and despair? Her brilliant, restless mind seethed as she listened and watched Max stride up and down, looking for once determined and sure.

"I won't *let* you abdicate," she said at last.

Her voice was quiet but it filled the room. Max stopped his pacing as if she had drawn him up sharply on a leash. He turned and looked at her. And Carlota stood up, tall, slim, commanding, a regal woman with an unearthly fire in her wide eyes.

"I'll go to Europe and force Napoleon to help! I'll shame him into aiding us. You are good and honest and fine. I won't let all you've worked for and dreamed of be sacrificed to malice and cowardice, just for the whim of one ugly little man."

Max took her in his arms and tried to soothe her as her voice rose. "You must not excite yourself so, my darling," he said, just as Leopold used to say, years ago, though Max did not know that. "You can't go to Europe alone. You aren't strong enough . . ."

"Strong!" Carlota laughed, a sound without mirth. "I am so strong . . . so strong, Max . . . You have no idea, you never have had any idea how strong I am. If I am there and can talk to them face to face I can shame Napoleon and Eugénie into keeping their promises. Listen . . ."

She talked long into the night, telling him what she would say, how she'd say it, what they'd say in return. She painted a picture for him, so triumphant, so compelling—above all so utterly reasonable, that Max at last, exhausted, gave in.

Carlota could always convince him. She had so much force. "So much more force than *I* have," he thought sadly, when he had agreed and she slept the sleep of utter exhaustion.

Sometimes that force of hers almost frightened him.

Carlota left Mexico July 9, 1866. Max escorted her part of the way to Veracruz and when they parted it was he who cried.

"Poor Maxl," Carlota said, stroking his hair. "I'll come back and take care of you as soon as I can. You must be brave." For herself, it seemed as if she were leaving part of herself behind. "My precious treasure," was what she always called Max. And to her he was just that: a treasure she must protect and cherish.

But Carlota had no idea of what faced her in France. Napoleon was a sick man, old, tired and broken. Worst of all, he had lost all confidence in Eugénie. She had been so wrong about Mexico that now he would take her advice about nothing.

"Never speak to me about Mexico again," he had told her. "It makes me ill. It has cost me popularity, money, and even, I think sometimes, my health."

In the Austrian-Prussian War, Austria was defeated by Prussia in a great battle. This frightened Napoleon almost out of his wits. He feared that if Prussia conquered Austria, France would be next on Prussia's list. Prussia would have a victorious, experienced army and his own troops were not even mobilized.

It was the worst possible time for Carlota to approach him. He had no time or heart for Mexican affairs.

Carlota arrived at the French port of Saint-Nazaire and Almonte and his wife came to meet her. The whole town turned out and the mayor came in his official robes to welcome her.

She telegraphed Napoleon also that she must see him at once to discuss Mexican matters. She did, however, think to add that it would give her pleasure to see him and Eugénie again.

There was not a sign of anyone from Napoleon's court.

"This is an insult. How dare he treat me so?" Carlota raged.

She, the Empress of all Mexico, had to drive to the Grand Hotel in a hired carriage. Never in her royal life had such a thing happened to her. When the French emissaries came rushing in, out of breath and full of apologies, explaining that they had gone to the wrong station, she did not know whether to believe them or not. The episode started her visit off badly and put her on the defensive at once.

The chief aide-de-camp of Napoleon carried a message from Eugénie asking when Carlota would like to receive her on the following day. "And her Majesty wished me to ask you how long you intend remaining in Paris," the aide added, his eyes curious.

"I shall stay in Paris," Carlota told him firmly. "I no longer have any relatives whom I can visit. You may tell her Majesty that I shall be glad to receive her at any time convenient to her."

Eugénie arrived at two the next day. She brought a large suite with her and Carlota sent three of her own attendants to wait for the Empress at the foot of the staircase. She herself, with Castillo, her minister, awaited Eugénie in her suite, as befitted an empress. And it was as an empress, not as a friend, that she was meeting Eugénie.

"I am pleased to see you again, my sister," Carlota said. *How old and grave she looks. Her face is ravaged*, Carlota thought as she took Eugénie in her arms and kissed her on both cheeks. The two empresses shut the door of the suite, leaving their attendants outside.

Carlota plunged into the story of Maximilian's troubles at once. As Eugénie listened, she seemed all warm, grave sympathy.

"She did not weep, but I had the feeling that tears were rising in her heart," Carlota wrote to Max that night.

But that was the most baffling interview Carlota had ever had. She would be explaining brilliantly, reasonably, logically, just how impossible it was for Max to rule a country which had never been pacified and Eugénie would say: "How is dear Max? He is so charming."

"Max is well. As well as can be expected. He bears his misfortunes nobly at a court where so many are against him," Carlota said.

"Oh, tell me about your court ceremonial," Eugénie interrupted. "Do you really have such splendid evening parties? And is Cuernavaca really as beautiful as Max writes us it is? How lucky you are, my dear, to live in such a paradise . . ."

It was maddening. Carlota felt as if she were trying to talk sense while a swarm of mosquitoes buzzed round her head, distracting her. And yet . . . And yet . . . Eugénie was so pleasant, so cordial, so interested. At last the Empress rose to go.

"I've overstayed my time frightfully," she said. "But then Mexico will always interest me."

She kissed Carlota warmly.

"And when may I return your Majesty's call?" Carlota asked.

Eugénie said, "Why not come the day after tomorrow? That is, if you really wish to call."

If she *wished* to call! Carlota drew a quick impatient breath. "And the Emperor? I shall see him too, then?"

"Poor dear. He's still unwell," Eugénie said lightly.

"I would rather visit you tomorrow," Carlota said suddenly. "And I shall insist on seeing the Emperor. Even if I have to break in!"

Next day, August 11, 1866, an imperial carriage came to fetch Carlota from the hotel. Like any woman who had been long away from the fashion centers, Carlota had spent the morning fussing over her costume. She didn't want to look provincial before the French court.

"Is my gown very wrinkled?" she kept asking Señora del Barrio. "Don't you think it best, after all, to wear the black, under the circumstances? But the black is still more wrinkled and there's not time to have it pressed." She sighed. "Well, at least my hat is the latest thing."

They had bought the hat that morning. It was large and white and it set off Carlota's rich beauty wonderfully. At the last moment she added a black lace mantilla to give herself a Mexican touch. "I look a fright," she told herself nervously as she snatched a last glance in the mirror.

She did not. As always, nervousness had heightened her color, brightened her eyes. The French people in the streets through which she drove cheered her and admired as only the French could admire beauty. Her hands stopped shaking and her poise came back as she bowed to them.

She was received at the palace with splendor. The whole imperial household was gathered at the foot of the stairs to welcome her. She walked up the staircase leading to the royal apartments between two lines of the Imperial Guard in their bearskins. The Empress waited for her at the head of the stairs and kissed her with affection.

As Carlota walked forward slowly, regally, to greet Napoleon, she spoke the words she'd memorized to begin her plea: "Sir, I have come to save a cause which is your own," she said solemnly. She laid before him the memorandum Max had given her, along with a detailed financial statement.

Then she talked. She asked that Bazaine be recalled; that money be continued to pay the troops; that troops be left in Mexico till Juárez was conquered. Her voice was low and very moving when she described Maximilian's dangerous position.

"I beg of you to remember the promises you have made us," she ended.

Napoleon had blinked like a crusty old turtle when she began. By the time she finished, tears were rolling down his cheeks. He looked at his wife so helplessly that Carlota was appalled.

Napoleon spoke at last, huskily. "Help does not depend upon my will. I am unable to do anything."

"Let me see the ministers, if they are the ones who are holding you back," Carlota urged. "I know I can convince them."

"I'll talk to them again myself," Napoleon said evasively. With that Carlota had to be content.

On the way back to her hotel, Carlota lay back in the carriage, pale and spent. "My poor Max," she kept murmuring. "My poor Max, so alone, so far away."

Carlota left Paris on a special train, provided by Napoleon, on August 23. She was going to take refuge at Miramar till she heard from Max what he wished her to do next. She enjoyed the journey. And when she crossed the Italian frontier she felt a surge of relief. "Thank God that I am leaving France where *he* lives and poisons the air by his villainy." She always spoke of Napoleon as *he*, after that. Her obsession about him increased daily.

Meantime Max followed, as best he could, Carlota's progress in Europe. He was dreadfully worried about her. He could not understand some of her letters at all. They sounded wild and strange.

He sent her a cable telling her that he had turned over all customhouses to the French, as they had once asked, in return for a written promise from Bazaine that he would pacify the country.

The customs revenues were the only source of money Mexico had left and Max had not wanted to give them up. But he had at last. And now he complained to Carlota that Bazaine was doing nothing to conquer the country but, on the contrary, was moving his troops out of town after town. The Juáristas instantly moved into each town and were even fighting near Veracruz.

This news startled Carlota into desperate action. "I cannot sit here idle while Max is threatened; while those savages are as close to him as Veracruz," she thought feverishly. "I must do something—quickly."

There was only one thing left to do. Much as she hated it, in view of all that had happened, she must appeal to the Pope. If she could persuade him to intercede with Napoleon, Max might yet be saved.

Her audience with the Pope was set for eleven in the morning on September 27. She was received with great pomp. The Papal Guards, in their uniforms designed so long ago by Michelangelo, lined the great staircase as she ascended.

The Pope, surrounded by his suite, awaited her in the throne room. He was very gracious. When she would have kissed his toe, as was customary, he lifted her so that she might kiss his ring, instead. Then he took her into another room where they could be alone.

Carlota entered that room with composure, as if in full control of her senses. When she came out of it, she had completely lost her mind.

Who can say just when it was that Carlota realized that this last resort had failed her? Did she listen to the Pope's evasions, to his final kindly explanation that he could do nothing for her, with her head throbbing and a mist rising before her great staring eyes? Did something snap in her brain at that moment? We do not know.

She drove back to the hotel with Señora del Barrio and spoke not one word. Her face was so drawn, so tragic, that the good woman dared not speak to her. Once in her room Carlota dismissed everyone and shut herself in. "I shall dine alone," she said. "And please send word that all further public ceremonies must be canceled."

She slept not at all that night. It seemed to her she could not bear it if she did not have a drink of water. Yet she dared not drink from the carafe provided for her. It was sure to be poisoned. By eight next morning she was dressed and ringing frantically for Señora del Barrio.

"We must drive to the fountain of Trevi," she cried. When they got there she leaped from the carriage and drank from the fountain as if she could never get enough. How delicious it was! Her lips were parched and dry with thirst and fever.

To Señora del Barrio's consternation Carlota ordered the

coachman to drive to the Vatican. It was only a little after eight in the morning. The Pope was at breakfast when she was shown in and he was astounded at sight of her, dressed in deep mourning, trembling with agitation. She threw herself at his feet, sobbing as if her heart would break. "My whole suite must be arrested. I'm surrounded by spies of Napoleon who wish my death. Only you can protect me," she cried.

He tried to soothe her. He lifted her and told her that she was mistaken. But her agitation increased. Finally he gave orders, privately, that her people at the hotel had better leave for the time. He also whispered to someone to telegraph the Count of Flanders, Carlota's younger brother, that he must come at once.

Her brother arrived on October 7, and in a few days he took her home to Miramar. In the weeks that followed, it was difficult to interest her in anything. Only politics still interested her, and about them she would talk quite rationally except that she saw the future in terms of mysticism. And always she saw her beloved Max at the most shining pinnacle of the world. Max would not fail. He would rule the world. She was certain of that.

That was her dream. She lived in it and upon it. Was it, perhaps, a blessing that she never knew how things went with Max? It is a temptation to think so. He remained for her, the shining, perfect knight, the fortunate and happy prince. She would have given her life for him gladly. And in a way she did.

So ended the girl Carlota, the regal girl who wanted too much from life. She was brave, she was kind, she took the obligations of royalty with intense seriousness. She wanted to do good as well as to be great. Most of all she wanted these things for the man she loved better than she had ever loved herself.

The girl Carlota was gone. But Carlota, the woman, lived to a great age. As late as 1926, visitors to Belgium could catch sometimes a fleeting glimpse of a tiny, fragile old lady walking in her gardens behind the high iron railings.

She lived those long years in dreams of her grandeur. To herself she was always a great empress. And Max, her beloved treasure, was forever a great emperor.

GEOFFREY TREASE

Victoria

Queen Victoria reigned for sixty-three years, seven months, and two days—the longest reign known in English history. Perhaps one of her greatest accomplishments throughout these years was that she brought back to the English throne what had been lacking for so long—the love and respect of the English people.

"THEY are the worst millstones about the necks of any government that can be imagined," declared the Duke of Wellington—though, being the Duke of Wellington and famous for his barrack-square language, he used a stronger adjective than "worst."

He went on with a seasoning of oaths better left out here: "They have insulted—*personally* insulted—two-thirds of the gentlemen of England. How can it be wondered at if they take their revenge on 'em in the House of Commons? It's their only opportunity and I think they're quite right to use it."

The millstones were the royal family. The occasion was in 1818 when, to the delight of the Iron Duke, Parliament had thrown out a proposal to pay increased allowances to some of the King's younger sons when they got married.

That was how the majority of Englishmen felt about the royal

From SEVEN QUEENS OF ENGLAND, by Geoffrey Trease.

family at the time. It was the atmosphere into which a princess, Alexandrina Victoria, was born just a year later, on May 24, 1819, in that same palace of Kensington in which Queen Anne had died one hundred and five years before.

England had prospered in the meantime. Though she had lost her American colonies, she had gained Canada, a large part of India, and other possessions. She had just won the greatest war in her history; Waterloo was a recent memory and Napoleon was still alive, exiled on a South Atlantic island. Yet never had the royal family been so disliked and despised.

What were the reasons?

The old King, George III, was pitied more than anything else. He was entering the last months of his sixty-year-long reign. He was blind, deaf, and insane. His past faults no longer stirred people to indignation—it was so long since the Declaration of Independence in 1776, so long since his stubborn stupidity had goaded the American colonists to revolution. But, if he was too old and feeble to be blamed, he was equally unable to inspire love or respect.

His kingly duties were carried out for him by the Prince Regent, soon to succeed him as George IV. "Prinny" had once been popular enough to win a nickname. He was, at least, a full-blooded, fast-living, gay dog of a prince, who had charmed one section of English society, while shocking the rest. But of late years he had gone to pieces, grown absurdly and revoltingly fat, and disgusted even many of his old followers by the natural coarseness which lay beneath his thin cover of elegance.

"Prinny" was the eldest of the King's fifteen children. Eleven of the others were still alive. Whereas he, at least, served as Prince Regent, the others did little or nothing to earn their keep. They were, as the Duke remarked, millstones about the necks of the government.

They had not even, up to then, provided the King with any grandchildren to carry on the royal line. What would happen when George III died, as soon he must? The crown would pass first to the childless Prince Regent; then, at his death (and he was neither young nor healthy), to each of his surviving brothers and sisters in turn. There might be a fresh coronation every year or two as one elderly, childless sovereign followed another. And then what—when the last died?

The whole situation was ridiculous.

It was not surprising if many intelligent Englishmen turned to the idea of a republic. If the royal line was to die out in any case, why wait? Why put up with these expensive, ill-mannered, and often immoral, German princelings for another twenty or thirty years?

For Germans they were, through and through. George I had had only a little Stuart blood. Each of his successors—even George III who "gloried in the name of Briton"—had taken a German wife. Though the Hanoverian kings had learnt to talk English they had become even more German in blood, rather than less.

Few people remember today that Victoria was almost entirely German and that her successor, Edward VII, a monarch of our own twentieth century, was if possible slightly more so.

That Victoria triumphed over these circumstances—that she made the royal family loved and respected and made herself the living symbol of the British Empire—was the really personal achievement of her reign.

Her father was Edward, Duke of Kent, the King's fourth son. He was no more attractive than the other Hanoverian princes. Once, as commander in chief, he had sentenced a soldier to nine hundred and ninety-nine lashes. Again, at Quebec—for he had spent some time in Canada—he had sentenced another man to death for desertion and mutiny. He had made the prisoner dress in his graveclothes and march two miles to the gallows with the coffin carried before him and the band playing a funeral march behind him. At the end of this ghastly ceremony the Duke graciously informed him that his life would, after all, be spared.

It is small wonder that such princes did not win the hearts of their subjects and a great mercy that the future queen grew up without the influence of such a father. For he died while she was a baby, so that she inherited only his blood—not his ideas of discipline.

A much greater influence was, naturally, her mother Victoria Mary Louisa, Princess of Saxe-Coburg-Saalfeld. She had been married before to the Prince of Leiningen and had two children, a boy, Charles, who had succeeded his father at Leiningen and a girl, Feodore, who was twelve when her half-sister Victoria was born.

The Duke of Kent married this young widow without any marked enthusiasm. Two of the other royal millstones, his brothers, married about the same time and with the same idea. The House of Hanover must somehow continue. Within a year or two the dying King was at last a grandfather several times over. One of the other babies came before Victoria in the line of succession but lived only for three months. When the Duke of Kent died of pneumonia in January, 1820, and it was certain that Victoria would never have a brother to displace her, it became very probable that, if she lived long enough, she would be Queen of England.

The Duke died at the south Devon seaside resort of Sidmouth. From there, the Duchess and her baby daughter returned to Kensington Palace where they had a suite of rooms which was their home for the next seventeen years. With them lived Feodore, fast developing into a lovely girl, with a natural tendency to spoil her plump little blue-eyed sister. And there was Feodore's governess, Fräulein Lehzen, daughter of a poor German pastor— described by the late Dame Edith Sitwell in her *Victoria of England* as "a very soberly dressed parrot, with her sharp black eyes snapping . . . with her bird-thin mouth that was drawn in because of her habit of eating caraway seeds, with her glossy black head cocked on one side so that her sharp ears might catch any whisper, any rumor of indiscreet conduct . . ." She became Victoria's governess too and a great influence over her; and "Prinny" (now George IV) tossed her a Hanoverian title with good-humored contempt, so that she became Baroness Lehzen, though there was no Baron Lehzen to match.

The mother was in striking contrast to the governess.

Here was no black-eyed parrot but a brown-eyed, brown-haired, rosy-cheeked, bustling, fat little woman, fond of gay colors and fonder of talking than listening. The governess tried hard to be discreet, though she did not always succeed: the Duchess did not even try and was continually causing upsets in the royal family.

Though Baroness Lehzen was Victoria's governess, she was not expected to teach her much in the way of ordinary book learning and what were called, in those days, "accomplishments." For these there was the usual team of tutors, captained by a clergyman, the Rev. George Davys, who had supervised her studies from the tender age of four. The organist of St. Margaret's, Westminster, came to teach her music and singing; a Royal Academician taught her to draw; a public-school master, from Westminster School, struggled none too successfully to instill a knowledge of English grammar; there was a French dancing-mistress for the minuet—ballroom dancing in couples, as we understand it, was only just coming in with the fashionable but rather shocking waltz, but it was not yet necessary for a princess to learn it for she could not whirl round the room with any partner of common birth; there were other specialists for French and German and, as she grew older, she was treated to lectures by scientific professors on such subjects as Cohesion and Capillary Attraction.

Baroness Lehzen was more concerned with forming her character, which was good but by no means perfect. "Never have I seen such a passionate and naughty child," she declared more than once. But she was truthful, the Baroness admitted, at whatever the cost. Nothing would tempt her to lie. That was a deeply ingrained quality which Time never altered. Not even kindness or courtesy would allow her to soften the literal truth. She always detested Gladstone, the great Liberal Prime Minister, who served her and the country so honestly for more than half a century. Yet, when he came to say good-bye for the last time—old and worn out in health—she could not bring herself to say "thank you" for what he had done. She was not sorry to see him go. Choosing her words carefully and alluding to his deafness and failing eyesight, she said: "I am sorry for the cause of your resignation." When he died, and the whole country paid tribute to him, she merely commented: "I never liked him, and I will say nothing about him."

When she said that, she was a queen and a very old woman nearing the end of her own course. But at the time of the Baroness's criticisms she was a small girl, strictly controlled, and not supposed even to suspect that she would ever wear the Crown of England.

Victoria was no fool. Any child of her age was quite capable of looking round the family, listing her uncles and aunts and cousins, and weighing up her own prospects. If there was a fool at Kensington it was the Baroness—if she really believed that Victoria knew nothing of her future until she was eleven when the Baroness coyly slipped a copy of the family tree inside her history book.

She was only six when she told another small girl, Lady Jane Ellice: "You must not touch these toys, they're mine. And I may call you Jane but you must not call me Victoria." And before she was nine Sir Walter Scott wrote in his journal, after dining at Kensington Palace: "This little lady is educated with so much care, and watched so closely, that no busy maid has a moment to whisper, 'You are heir to England.' I suspect, if we could dissect the little heart, we should find that some pigeon or bird of the air had carried the matter."

George IV died soon after her eleventh birthday. Uncle William became king. Some called him "the sailor king," because he had served in the Navy under Nelson and was keenly interested in the sea. Others called him, less respectfully, "Silly Billy." He was not without common sense, though, and certainly not without kindly feelings. His chief lack was good manners.

Victoria did not go to the Coronation. She spent the day in floods of tears, like any other disappointed girl. Her mother had started the seven-year wrangle with the new king which was to end only at his death and her daughter's accession. The Duchess of Kent was like a ruffled hen with one chick: all she could think of now was Victoria's rights and position as heir-presumptive to the throne. She had begun by writing to the Duke of Wellington, as Prime Minister, demanding an allowance for her daughter from the King: the Duke had answered politely that the King fully intended giving her one but he could do nothing till Parliament voted on the whole question of the royal incomes. There were further brushes between them, the Duke behaving as usual like a gentleman, the mother ignorantly, rudely, and absurdly, like any foolish woman determined to stand on her dignity and put her opponent in his place. On the one matter of the Coronation, King William was, strictly speaking, at fault. He arranged that, in the order of precedence, his brothers should come before her and her daughter; whereas, since her dead husband had been an elder brother, his widow and child should have occupied a similar senior position.

It is hard for those who have never lived in a stiff, formal society to appreciate how this question of precedence—the exact order of a procession, the seating at a banquet table, even the difference between driving in a carriage with one's back to the horses and facing them—can become a matter of life and death. It is still something which whitens the hair of diplomats and private secretaries. It was certainly not less vital in the England of 1830.

The Duchess stuck to her guns. She was not going to the Coronation if it meant taking second place to her brothers-in-law. A child's passionate disappointment meant nothing. She took Victoria off to the Isle of Wight and wrote to say that the princess was not well enough for either of them to attend.

William IV liked his niece and would gladly have seen more of her. It was right that he should have done so, for he was an elderly man and it was practically certain that she would be the next sovereign. The Duchess was all in favor of preparing Victoria for what lay ahead—but any grooming of the future queen was for her to do, with the help of her brother Leopold. He had just accepted the crown of Belgium, a newly created kingdom, but he liked nothing better than writing long letters of advice to his niece and was not unwilling to rule England, as well as Belgium, by remote control.

From the age of thirteen Victoria began to travel round the country with her mother, making herself known to the people who would one day be her subjects. They stayed at great country houses such as the Duke of Devonshire's stately mansion at Chatsworth in the Derbyshire dales. King William lent his royal yacht to the niece he was scarcely allowed to see and they sometimes traveled by water.

Victoria was now keeping a journal, so that her life during her teens is very easy to picture. She wrote of her journeys and impressions; of her pony, "sweet little Rosa," and her mother's "dear sweet little Dash," a King Charles spaniel; of the new bridge she declared open at Chester and the cotton mills she visited in Derbyshire and the foundation stone she laid at a boys' school in Wales. Nor did she leave out her assessment of the boy-cousins who came over to visit her from Germany: "They are both extremely tall. Alexander is very handsome and Ernest has a very kind expression. . . . We shall miss them at breakfast, at luncheon, at dinner, riding, driving, sailing, walking, in fact everywhere."

The habit of underlining almost every other word was one which remained with her in later years. She also resorted to a plentiful use of full capitals and peppered her journals and letters with exclamation marks. She was always an emphatic person and she knew no more subtle ways of making her opinion clear.

Birthdays, as might be expected, figured prominently in her records. "How very old ! !" she wrote at fourteen. The King insisted on giving her a juvenile ball at St. James's Palace and her mother could not very well refuse. It was a wonderful evening. The King led her in to supper himself, as the guest of honor, and the Queen sat on the other side of her, and everybody drank her health, and she danced no fewer than eight quadrilles, and it was well after midnight when she drove home to Kensington.

But how young fourteen seemed when she was sixteen! "I feel," she wrote, "that the two years to come till I attain my eighteenth birthday are the most important of any almost. I now only begin to appreciate my lessons and hope from this time on to make great progress." This time the main birthday treat was a concert at Kensington Palace arranged by her mother, with all the stars from the Opera engaged.

Seventeen was marked by a ball, but a grown-up affair this time and at Kensington, not St. James's. The Duchess of Kent was quite capable of giving a ball for her own daughter, without any help from the King. . . . This time the boy-cousins who came over from Germany included Prince Albert of Saxe-Coburg, three months younger than herself, and she liked him best of all, which was fortunate because her scheming Uncle Leopold was already intent on getting them married. She finished the evening as his partner in a country dance at half-past three in the morning.

"Allow me then, my dearest Uncle," she wrote to King Leopold, "to tell you how delighted I am with him in every way. He possesses every quality that could be desired to make me perfectly happy. He has besides the most pleasing and delightful exterior you can possibly see."

The boy's impressions of the visit were given in a letter to his stepmother. The English climate made him bilious and he could not stand the long hours—he could hardly keep awake after midnight. "Aunt Kent was very kind," he added, "and our cousin also is very amiable." He was a serious, studious youth and Victoria had not the intellect to meet him on his favorite ground—even her musical taste was superficial compared with his. But he had a strong sense of duty and would do what was expected of him.

There was one person who looked forward to Victoria's eighteenth birthday even more anxiously than she did herself. It was the King.

He was in failing health. The Duchess infuriated him more and more. "That woman is a nuisance!" he would cry, reading in his newspaper that she had been pushing herself forward again. His one fear was that he might die before his niece became eighteen and old enough to rule by herself. He could not bear to think of "that nuisance of a woman" acting, through her daughter, as the uncrowned Queen of England.

A climax arrived when they came to stay at Windsor the day

before his own birthday banquet. Having public business in London, he paid a surprise visit to Kensington and found that she had moved into a suite of seventeen rooms not only without his permission but in direct defiance of the orders he had given. Boiling with rage he returned to Windsor and marched into the drawing room where the family guests for the next day's banquet were gathered for the evening. He went first to Victoria, took both her hands affectionately, and declared that he only wished he saw her more often. Then he bowed coldly to her mother and remarked in a distinct voice, for all the room to hear, that he had just come from Kensington where "a most unwarrantable liberty" had been taken with one of his palaces. He did not understand conduct so disrespectful to him and he would not endure it. There was a painful silence after he had spoken. It was the stillness before the storm which broke at the birthday banquet next day.

It was a splendid occasion. There were a hundred royal and noble guests ranged along the tables. The myriad candles flickered softly on gold plate and jewels, on uniforms and sashes, on rich gowns and bare shoulders. Powdered flunkeys stole about in the background or stood like statues. The King's health was drunk with due ceremony. Victoria faced her uncle across the table and smiled over her glass. Her mother, placed at his right hand, drank and was no doubt glad that he could not look into her eyes.

The King rose to make a speech in reply. And instead of the pleasantries usual on such an occasion he let forth a stream of angry eloquence which paralyzed the diners and froze even the flunkeys behind their chairs. If he had been an admiral, denouncing a mutineer from his quarterdeck, he could scarcely have said more.

The Princess Victoria would be eighteen next year. He hoped and prayed he might be spared for that period so that there would be no risk of a regency by—he grew scarlet as his anger mounted—"a person now near to me, who is surrounded by evil advisers and who is herself incompetent to act with propriety in the station in which she would be placed."

There was a gasp round the table. Queen Adelaide went pink with embarrassment. Truly, William had been sorely provoked but really a public banquet was no place——

The Duchess was white as death. Tears trembled in Victoria's eyes as her uncle went on.

"I have no hesitation in saying . . ." Certainly the rough-tongued old sailor had no hesitation: it was all too plain that he had very great pleasure. ". . . that I have been insulted grossly and continuously insulted by that person—but I am determined no longer to endure a course of behavior so disrespectful to me. Amongst many other things I have particularly to complain of is the manner in which this young lady has been kept away from my Court. She has been repeatedly kept from my drawing rooms, at which she ought always to have been present—but I am fully resolved this shall not happen again. I would have her know that I am King and I am determined to make my authority respected. For the future I shall insist and command that the Princess do upon all occasions appear at my Court, as it is her duty to do."

The broadside had its effect. When the other guests had gone, the Duchess called for her carriage and declared she would drive back to London that night. She was persuaded, however, to stay at Windsor until the next day. She did not dare to ignore the King's words and from that time onwards Victoria was regularly seen at Court. But the King would see! Or rather—most unfortunately—he would not see, because he would be dead by then. Under or over the age of eighteen Victoria was a dutiful daughter and, even when Queen, would always listen to her natural guide and adviser, that unselfish Mama whose whole life had been given up to her protection and education and whose bedroom she still shared wherever she went. What Mama could not grasp herself would be taken care of by Mama's dear brother Leopold. The child always listened to *him* with proper respect. "He is so clever, so mild and so prudent," wrote the Princess—was it entirely for her own satisfaction she wrote, or for her mother's eyes? "He alone can give me good advice on everything. To hear dear Uncle speak on any subject is like reading a highly instructive book. . . ." Is it possible that Victoria had more sense of humor than is sometimes supposed?

Her eighteenth birthday arrived. The King had been seriously ill, but he clung to life if only to annoy his sister-in-law, and recovered sufficiently for the celebrations to take place as planned, though he was not able to attend the Court ball given in Victoria's honor. He sent her a grand piano as a birthday present and followed it with a direct offer—over her mother's head—of a ten-thousand-pound-a-year allowance. This vexed the Duchess. Four thousand pounds, she felt, would have been quite enough for so young a person and the other six thousand should have been given to her to spend on Victoria's behalf.

There was little time left for further squabbling. Within a few weeks it was known that the King's days were numbered, and on June 20, 1837, very early in the morning, he died.

"I was awoke at 6 o'clock by Mama," wrote the new Queen in her journal, "who told me that the Archbishop of Canterbury and Lord Conyngham were here and wished to see me. I got out of bed and went into my sitting room (only in my dressing gown) and alone, and saw them."

That significant word "alone" is repeated over and over again in her entry for that first day of her reign. She saw Lord Melbourne, the Prime Minister—she held her first Council—she received four State officials—she had dinner . . . in every case, alone. She seemed suddenly a new person, with a power and dignity and independence which nobody (least of all her mother) had ever suspected. The Duke of Wellington, coming away from her Council, said: "She not only filled her chair, she filled the room."

There were many instructions to give on that first crowded eventful day, but there was one in particular which she must have waited—how long?—to give.

Her bed was to be moved out of Mama's room. In future the Queen would sleep alone.

Mama and "my dear Lehzen" and clever Uncle Leopold soon found that their influence was over. Leopold, writing long letters from Brussels, was naturally the slowest to realize it. His niece still answered charmingly but it became clear that, having read his advice, she went her own way. She had accepted his agent, Baron Stockmar, as a confidential adviser, always at her elbow . . . but somehow Britain continued to go Britain's way, not Belgium's. This rather plain, stocky girl of eighteen—who lamented to her first Prime Minister, Lord Melbourne, "Everyone grows but me!"—was quite determined to rule.

Yet, though she had an iron will and a deep sense of her position as Queen, she had also (what Elizabeth I never had) a feminine longing to lean on a stronger, masculine arm. She had not, like the great Tudor, a passion for complete independence. She *wanted* to depend. But the person on whom she depended must be worthy and chosen by herself, not by her mother.

In the first few years of her reign she depended on Lord Melbourne—that charming, amusing, rather wicked old gentleman, who taught her so much about public business, mixing his wise hints with jokes and compliments about her new tight sleeves or the fact that she had given up wearing her hair in curls.

From the day of her marriage she depended more and more—at last almost entirely—on her husband. And after his death there was the third long phase of her reign when she depended not on any living adviser but on the memory of the dead; judging everything by what *he* would have done, what *he* would have wished.

The fourth phase was dominated by the Conservative leader Disraeli until he too died in 1881. Like Melbourne, he was witty and shrewd—but he far outdid Melbourne in the flattery of his compliments. Whenever Disraeli was in power Victoria leaned happily on his support. When the Liberals won an election and her detested Gladstone took Disraeli's place as Prime Minister she showed him only cold civility and longed for the next Conservative victory.

During that same period, in her private household, she depended to an extraordinary extent on a remarkable Highland servant, John Brown, whom she had promoted from a gillie, a sort of gamekeeper, to be her personal attendant. He was an outspoken, whisky-loving creature who patted visiting statesmen on the back and addressed his royal mistress in more familiar terms than she would have borne from any other person alive; but she not only tolerated him, she liked him, and was grief-stricken when he died. Her treatment of John Brown was just another instance of this need to depend on someone—to have someone in the world who would give her instructions instead of receiving them, whether it was an adored husband, or a masterful servant bidding her drink up her tea.

Only in the last twenty years of her long reign was there no such dominating figure. But by then she was an old woman, fixed in her habits, ruling automatically, by instinct. Independent at last.

The story of Victoria is not the history of Victorian England.

The events of those sixty-three years cannot be fully told here, nor need they be, for they were not the Queen's doing. The time had gone by when an English queen could govern personally, almost without Parliament, as Elizabeth had done; or through a corrupt and managed Parliament as—to a great extent—Anne and the Georges had contrived to do.

The First Reform Act, passed when she was twelve, had wiped out any chance of that. Democracy was coming. The first years of her own reign were stormy with the demands of the Chartists —votes for every man, however poor; secret voting; salaries for Members of Parliament so that the working class could not only vote but provide their own candidates. Every one of the Chartist demands (except one, providing for a new Parliament each year) has since been granted and is now accepted as a natural part of the democratic heritage. But at the time they were revolutionary. Men armed and drilled to fight for them, men marched for them, and were shot down in the gutter. The Charter was refused at the cannon's mouth but the demands in it were granted later, one by one.

By the end of her reign democracy had arrived. Only the women's votes (of which she would have violently disapproved) were delayed a little longer.

Victoria favored some Prime Ministers much more than others. She did things which no modern queen would do. She was obstinate, she was sometimes interfering, but she never tried to fight Parliament or her ministers on any vital political question. She cannot be blamed—or praised—for most of the main happenings in her reign.

We are only concerned here with the part she was able to play in her own person.

First, coming to the throne as a gracious, well-bred girl, she made royalty popular as it had not been within living memory. Here, people felt, was no "millstone" but a sovereign they could love and respect.

Next, by her marriage and her family life afterwards, she set a new and infinitely higher standard than any of her relatives. The accent was on goodness. England was tired of the drunken, gambling, loose-living Hanoverians. Hard work, plain living, and high thinking were the ideals of the period.

She married her cousin Albert in 1840, before her twenty-first birthday. Remembering that she was a sovereign even before she was a young lady, she proposed to him. "Albert," she told the Duchess of Gloucester, "would never have presumed to take such a liberty as to propose to the Queen of England!" She was, not surprisingly, accepted.

"I will not let my courage fail," wrote the solemn youth to his tutor. "She is really most good and amiable, and I am quite sure Heaven has not given me into evil hands, and that we shall be happy together."

The wedding was small and quiet, not at the Abbey but at the little Chapel Royal of St. James's. She wore a white satin gown with a deep flounce of Honiton lace, with earrings and a necklace of diamonds. There was a banquet at Buckingham Palace, a two-day honeymoon at Windsor with dancing both evenings after dinner, and then the conscientious Queen hurried back to her public duties in London.

The question was, what part in those duties—if any part—was her husband to play?

None, said the country firmly, or at most purely ornamental. From the far-off days when Mary I had been married to Philip of Spain the English had been determined that no foreign prince should edge his way on to the throne merely by marrying their queen. William of Orange was quite a different matter, for he had been one of the family anyhow.

Albert should never be King. Prince Consort was the highest title they would give him. He was an entirely worthy young man, without any vices—and the contrary English, being the English, never liked him.

Victoria, however, adored him. Not even Mary II had been more under the spell of her husband. Victoria could not hand over her power to Albert as Mary had done to William III— but not even the Prime Minister could prevent her talking every question over with her clever, thoughtful Albert and afterwards repeating his opinions as though they were her own.

So Albert became a mighty power in the background. He had to begin in a small way, overhauling the organization of the royal palaces with German thoroughness, suggesting how money could be saved by the dismissal of a footman here or the use of one candle instead of two. Launching out a little, he planned her a new house at Osborne, in the Isle of Wight and then Balmoral, in the Highlands, a serious-looking mansion of granite, somewhat German in spirit but a wild riot of stags' heads and tartans inside. The chief architectural masterpiece he inspired, though, was the Crystal Palace, a really remarkable edifice of glass and bright blue iron girders, first erected for the Great Exhibition of 1851. The Exhibition itself was Albert's inspiration too: he had a boundless interest in science and industry, believing (like most men of his time) that humanity was moving steadily forward and that world peace and prosperity were just round the corner, to be achieved as soon as enough factories had been built and enough new inventions devised.

Gradually he began to have greater and greater political influence. He worked tirelessly through the masses of papers which continually arrived for Victoria's signature. He explained, suggested, and worded improvements. On the whole he was an influence for good. Without him Victoria might have been more stubborn in her disagreements with her ministers.

Their first child was born in November, 1840. It was a girl, Princess Victoria, but a son and heir, Prince Albert Edward, followed a year later. Three more sons and four more daughters completed, in due course, a family of typical nineteenth-century size. Most of them grew up and married into the various royal houses of Germany or Russia but only "Bertie"—later King Edward VII—played any important role in history.

Victoria's twenty-one years of married bliss were not matched by equal bliss for all her subjects. In 1845 the potato crop failed in Ireland and there was terrible famine. Three-quarters of a million people died, and over the next fifteen years, two and a half million more emigrated to America carrying with them a hatred of British government which smolders to this day.

From 1854 to 1856 there was the Crimean War, a pointless struggle between Russia on the one hand and Britain, France, and Turkey on the other, of which little is now remembered but the equally pointless (though heroic) Charge of the Light Brigade and the pioneer hospital work of Florence Nightingale. No sooner was peace made than the Indian Mutiny broke out, in 1857, with a sickening massacre of British women and children at Cawnpore and (what is less often taught in the schools of the West) counteratrocities committed against the natives of India by the British.

The American Civil War opened in 1861, bringing unemployment to the Lancashire mill workers through the stoppage in the raw cotton supply. But for the Prince Consort it might have had even more serious effects.

In 1861 the Prince caught cold inspecting the military college at Sandhurst. The sickness proved to be typhoid and two weeks later, on December 14, 1861, he died.

To Victoria it seemed that her own life was over. If anyone could have told her that nearly forty years of her reign still lay ahead she would have found it unbelievable—and unbearable.

She had been wrapped up in her husband and not even her nine children could console her. She had always had a morbid interest in death—many young people had, in those days, when even a private person was buried with pomp and pageantry and when mourning was a long-drawn-out drama of hushed voices and black clothes, with black edges even to handkerchiefs and writing paper. But few widows ever gave themselves up to grief as thoroughly as she did.

For ten years she shut herself up in retirement. She could not bear to appear in public. She still carried out her unavoidable duties as Queen—signed papers, read memoranda, received her Prime Minister—but that was all.

In those years of retirement Victoria threw away most of the popularity—the love, even—which she had won from her subjects earlier in the reign. Again, but for new reasons, republican ideas became widespread. Why pay out huge sums each year, people argued, for a sovereign who holds no Court and never drives out either to open a Parliament or to meet her people less formally?

It was, by a curious accident, her erring son who put a sudden stop to all that criticism. Bertie fell desperately ill with that same typhoid fever which had carried off his father. For two weeks he lay at death's door. The country waited breathless. All the former resentment against Victoria was swamped by sympathy. There were national rejoicings when he recovered and a service of thanksgiving at St. Paul's which the Prime Minister persuaded her to attend. Her drive to the cathedral was the cue for a tumultuous welcome from the crowd, and her old popularity came flooding back.

From then onwards Victoria let herself be drawn back, step by step, into public life. When Gladstone was replaced as Prime Minister by the amusing and charming Disraeli she was much more easily coaxed. She regained her old interest in affairs. She shared his dreams of a glorious expanding British Empire.

In 1887 she celebrated her Golden Jubilee, the fiftieth year of her reign. Ten years later followed the Diamond Jubilee and again the beacon fires blazed from hill to hill. She was very old now, and too lame to walk in any kind of ceremonial procession, but she drove six miles through London streets that were hedged with pink cheering faces and frenziedly waving flags.

She had come a long way. She had been born in the reign of George III and she had lived to see the little boy who would one day become George VI. Her reign was an age in itself, the Victorian Age.

What does that phrase stand for in most minds?

The Victorian Age doubled the population—to about thirty-four millions in 1900. Railways transformed the countryside. Not only houses and factories multiplied but hospitals, schools, and colleges. Britain became greater, richer, and healthier—though not, unfortunately, more beautiful. In science, industry, and the art of government it was a period of tremendous progress.

However bad its painting and sculpture, at least its literature was first-class. Dickens, Thackeray, the Brontës, George Eliot, Trollope, Meredith, and Hardy were its novelists. Tennyson, Browning, Morris, and Swinburne were its poets. Carlyle, Macaulay, and Ruskin were writing magnificent prose, each in his highly individual way. Even the young reader for the first time had a literature worth reading: it was the age of Charles Kingsley and Lewis Carroll, Rudyard Kipling and Robert Louis Stevenson. Even the theater flowered at the end of the period: two new playwrights were reviving the long-dead drama in the eighteen-nineties, Oscar Wilde and Bernard Shaw. Before that, Gilbert and Sullivan had conquered the world with their light operas. In the realm of more serious music Elgar was already at work.

In the Diamond Jubilee of 1897 those glories reached their climax. As the twentieth century dawned it began to look as though Victoria, like Elizabeth I, had outlived her own epoch.

She was eighty-one at the turn of the century. Very old, very tired, but still carrying out her duties, still keeping her journal, though now she dictated it because of her failing sight. The end came quickly and gently on January 22, 1901. The heralds got out their emblazoned uniforms to proclaim Bertie from the battlements of St. James's.

All the pronouns must be changed now. Few men alive could remember the time when they had sung "God Save the King."

ALDEN HATCH

Juliana of the Netherlands

Queen Juliana is a truly democratic ruler. When she ascended the throne of the Netherlands in 1948, she described the Dutch monarchy as "the rock amid wild waves," and her mother's reign as moving from the tradition-bound world of the nineteenth century to the modern viewpoint of the twentieth century.

Juliana's mother, Queen Wilhelmina, set the style for modern rulers who pass along the crown to the younger generation as a sign of trust, not of necessity.

QUEEN WILHELMINA was very tired. The War had cost her more than she let anyone realize, and the first years of peace were, perhaps, even more strenuous because of the ruined condition of her country, the Cabinet changes and new elections, and reorganizing her own entourage—mostly with people from the Resistance. Like Holland itself, her whole way of life had to be

From BERNHARD, PRINCE OF THE NETHERLANDS, by *Alden Hatch*.

rebuilt almost from scratch, and she had thrown herself into the task "flat out," as her devoted son-in-law would say. In the summer of 1947 she was even more weary, and began to talk again of her cherished plan of abdicating.

The Queen had been interested in the idea of abdication ever since her girlhood. In her autobiography *Lonely But Not Alone* she states the philosophical reasoning which reinforced her wish to pass the crown on to her daughter:

"When I studied history," she writes, "I was particularly struck by the abdication of the Emperor Charles V [of Spain] in 1555. I recognized the wisdom of it. The idea that there was such a thing as abdication was entirely new to me. Of course, I went and talked it over with Mother. . . . What interested me then, and continued to do so afterwards, was the sound idea expressed in it, that one should not continue in an office which requires enterprise, resolution, and energy, and which has to be supported by complete fitness, when one no longer feels oneself to possess these forces.

"Our constitution mentions abdication in Article 15. The element of free will (which this Article permitted me) may well have heightened my sense of responsibility and devotion to my task. . . .

"During the War, of course, the question of abdication never entered my thoughts. . . . It was only after the period of transition following the Liberation that I felt justified in seriously considering abdication. . . .

"Slowly we approached my sixty-eighth birthday, which coincided with the fiftieth anniversary of my reign. Large-scale plans were being made to celebrate this jubilee. I did not feel up to this sort of thing any more. . . .

"In the course of the years I had seen important decisions made everywhere in the world and in many different fields. It had often struck me that the efficacy of many decisions would have been better assured if they had been made, not by people nearing the end of their lives, but by people who were still in their prime.

"On no account did I want to give the impression that I was

staying on in order to have my jubilee—I who had signed the law on the retirement age for many of my countrymen. . . ."

When the Queen broached the subject of her abdication to her daughter and son-in-law, in the summer of 1947, the younger people were hardly elated. Juliana, in particular, was distressed. She dreaded the responsibility of being Queen and the inevitably increased glare of the spotlight. More important, she wanted to devote herself to her children, particularly little Marijke.

Bernhard too would have preferred that things remain in *statu quo*, since he foresaw that as the husband of the Queen his position would circumscribe even more his freedom of action, and his ceremonial duties would interfere with the work of military and economic reconstruction into which he had thrown himself so energetically. The doors of the "cage" were closing.

However, he saw that Queen Wilhelmina had made up her mind, and he knew that once a Dutchman or Dutchwoman did that it was useless to argue. Furthermore, he deeply sympathized with the Queen. As he pointed out to Juliana, her mother had done all—and more—that could be expected of a human being, however dedicated to her calling, in nearly fifty strenuous years of her reign, during which her world had changed more completely than in the five hundred years before that. She had earned a rest if ever a public servant had.

For her part, Juliana's sense of duty was as strong as her filial love. When it was put to her like that she could not but agree.

On one point Queen Wilhelmina did not get her way—her plan to abdicate *before* her fiftieth anniversary. When she sounded her advisers on the subject they pointed out that preparations for the jubilee were already begun, and it would be such a blow for the merchants and manufacturers of souvenirs, as well as for her disappointed subjects, that it would cast a cloud over the beginning of the new Queen's reign. They absolutely refused to have any part of it. Queen Wilhelmina writes, "I had a difficult, even a sad, time, during the following months, when I had to look for a solution all alone. . . ."

The compromise finally arrived at was that Wilhelmina would remain Queen long enough to receive the expressions of loyalty and devotion of the citizens of The Hague on her Golden Anniversary and make her festive entry into Amsterdam. Then she would immediately abdicate in favor of her daughter. The organizers of the jubilee, sighing with relief, agreed that this would be satisfactory.

Possibly as an unconscious gesture of revolt against the closing cage, Bernhard chose this period to grow a moustache. The Prince says, "My moustache was extremely ugly, a horrible reddish color. I grew it to see who my true friends were. The people who said, 'It's awful, cut it off,' were honest. Those who said, 'It's very nice,' I knew were lying. Of course, one's wife is the first to tell you the truth.

"Bedell Smith said, 'Have a moustache if you must, but don't let it droop. Makes you look like Molotov.'

"After I had had my fun I shaved it off. At my first public appearance after that there was a dead silence in the crowd, and then one woman shouted, 'Thank God it's off!' "

Because she was so very tired, and as a sort of rehearsal for her daughter, Queen Wilhelmina exercised her constitutional power to declare Juliana regent for a limited period beginning October 14, 1947. She writes: "I resumed my functions at the end of the term set. Juliana had had an opportunity to get an idea of the task that awaited her."

Juliana already had an extremely clear idea of that task, having studied law, and especially Dutch Constitutional Law, very earnestly at the University of Leiden. Unlike Great Britain, which has no written constitution, the function of Dutch monarchs is spelled out in precise legal language by the Constitution enacted in 1814, but amended several times since. Its basic principle is that, "The King is inviolable; the Ministers are responsible," which in effect means that the Crown possesses but does not exercise power.

Where the Queen can really exercise a little more power than a British sovereign is in the formation of a new government. She consults with the Vice-President of the Council of State—she is its President—the Presidents of the First and Second Chambers, and, of course, with the leaders of all the political parties, including the Communist. Having done so, however, she is at liberty to use her own judgment about whom to ask to form a government. This person is called the Formateur and is not necessarily the proposed President of the Council of Ministers (Prime Minister). Sometimes he is not even in the new Cabinet.

If the Formateur cannot get together a Cabinet which can win a vote of confidence of the States-General he has to resign and somebody else has to try it. However, the very fact that the Queen has appointed him gives him considerable leverage with the deputies, and in this respect the Queen's choice is an exercise of real power. In this connection the Prime Minister, Dr. de Quay, said, "Another thing is that Queen Juliana's remarkable personality and her popularity also lend prestige to her choice."

The new government does not have to propose a program to the States-General *before* they are nominated. After nomination they decide on this program, and it is submitted to the sovereign with their names. They are then appointed by royal decree. This system also gives the Queen a certain area of judgment.

The Queen has an even more important sphere of influence. According to R. K. Gooch in *Governments of Continental Europe:* "The [Dutch] monarchs are something more than formal and ceremonial Heads of State. . . . The monarch, standing above parties, plays a role essential to parliamentary government. So far as personal influence in the political sphere is concerned there exists . . . the right to be consulted, the right to encourage, the right to warn."

Given the devotion of the Dutch to the House of Orange and their personal love for their Queen, this is a very great right indeed, and a heavy responsibility.

Knowing these things and pondering them virtually all her life, Juliana was prepared for the task she assumed as Regent. But she was surprised by the enormous amount of paper work involved. The "right to be consulted" meant that every important action of every Minister had to be submitted to her and the necessary documents had to be signed by her. Since she was too conscientious, too Dutch, ever to sign a paper she had not thoroughly read, this meant hours of studying long, intricate legal

documents. Bernhard could not help her here. Extremely punc-
tilious about constitutional limitations, he would not even have
wanted to look at them. In this he was quite different from
Queen Victoria's Prince Consort, who read everything and practically guided his wife's hand as she signed the royal documents.

However, there is nothing in the Constitution to prevent Bernhard expressing his opinions like any other Dutch citizen. In
fact, that is exactly what he is legally—just another Dutchman.
Once he jokingly said, "I think I'll found a new political party
and run for Prime Minister."

In actual fact Bernhard breaks the electoral law every four
years. Every Dutchman of legal age is required by law to vote in
the general elections, or at least come to the polls, or be subject
to a fine. Bernhard has scrupulously refrained from doing so.
There is no record of his being fined.

However, his meticulous determination to remain above party
does not muzzle him on matters about which he cares deeply,
such as the economic life of Holland and the unification of
Western Europe. Juliana, like many of her people and, indeed,
many Europeans, knows his opinions. Whether she is influenced
by them is another matter.

Queen Wilhelmina was still troubled about how to tell the
Dutch people her decision. The situation was somewhat com-
plicated by the fact that a new government was soon to be
formed. She solved it by broadcasting the news to the people on
May 12, 1948, the ninety-ninth anniversary of her own father's
installation as king in 1849. At the same time she appointed
Juliana regent again for a term ending a few days before Wilhelmina's sixty-eighth birthday, when she would resume the Crown
for the hail-and-farewell ceremonies. The purpose of the second
regency was so that Juliana would begin her reign with a government formed on her own initiative.

On August 31, 1948, Queen Wilhelmina's sixty-eighth birthday, the jubilee began in The Hague. But the great ceremonies
were reserved for Amsterdam, the state capital. For these occasions Bernhard, Juliana, and the four children went to stay at

the Dam Palace, a huge structure in the seventeenth-century style built originally as Amsterdam's Town Hall. Its great hall, intended for assemblies of burghers, is the largest in Europe, and many of the other 175 rooms, including the royal suite, are on a similar scale, with lofty ceilings which tend to make mere human beings feel exceedingly small.

Here on the morning of September 4, 1948, a group of very solemn people were gathered at a long table in the magnificent but cheerless salon known as the Moses Room. Princess Juliana was there dressed in a smart tailored suit, with a rather large pillbox hat cocked over one eye. Prince Bernhard wore his uniform of an admiral in the Netherlands navy, splendid with the ribbons of his orders, both those given him because of his position and those he cherished because they had been fairly won in the field. The others at the table were mostly government and court officials in formal morning dress, here to perform their proper functions.

To them came Queen Wilhelmina, radiating vitality and happiness. This was the final stage of a long road whose penultimate moments had been her last arrival in Amsterdam as Queen, and the great rally in the Stadium, which symbolized both her Golden Jubilee and her farewell. There she had been greeted by such an outpouring of love and loyalty as few monarchs ever see.

The purpose of the meeting in the Moses Room was business, and the Queen was appropriately dressed in a severely tailored suit and a large no-nonsense beret. Her cheerfulness was genuine, compound of relief at the prospect of freedom from responsibility, and pride in the beauty and intelligence of her daughter. She wrote: "How numerous were my reasons for gratitude! In the first place my confidence in Juliana's warmth of feeling for the people we both love so much and in her devotion to the task awaiting her. . . . Then also the fact that I might have the opportunity to see something of her reign. Really there was no room for sadness in my heart. . . ."

Sensing the dismal atmosphere of the company, Queen Wilhelmina made an extra effort to cheer them up, and succeeded— temporarily.

The business of the meeting then got under way. It followed exactly the procedure when Queen Wilhelmina's great-grandfather (William I) abdicated in 1840. The Act of Abdication, to take effect at noon that day, was read aloud. Then the Queen signed it, followed by the witnesses. Wilhelmina says, "The simple ceremony was a wonderful experience."

There followed a long wait for noon to strike. Everybody had been so prompt and the ceremony so short that there was a good hour to go—it seemed like a year. They sat around the table trying to make small talk and fiddling with their watches. Despite Wilhelmina's best efforts the atmosphere got ever more tense. Juliana was particularly nervous, and Bernhard worked "like mad" to enliven things.

At last, with a whirr and a splendid clang of metal that made them all jump, the clock in the tower began to toll. They sat frozen in their seats counting the strokes that singing through brick and stone seemed to vibrate from the soles of their feet up through their bodies. For all of them knew that the clock was striking not an hour but an age.

When it was done Wilhelmina, the Princess of the Netherlands, as she had this moment become, jumped up briskly. She took her daughter by the hand and walked through the French window on to the balcony. A wave of cheering struck them with the palpable force of a hundred-mile wind. Below them the great brick-paved square of the Dam was packed with a crowd that flowed back up all the streets as far as—farther than—eye could see. Bernhard, following closely behind his wife, saw her sway a little, very much affected, and tighten her grip on her mother's hand.

Then Wilhelmina began to speak, and ten thousand people in the Square and twice ten thousand beyond sight of her, and every person in Holland who could get to a radio, were silent, straining to listen. The quietness and simplicity of her delivery made her words unbearably dramatic. People stood there transfixed, not moving at all, not knowing that tears were flowing down their intent faces. Bernhard saw Juliana was at breaking point, and made a half-gesture of protection toward her. Then, as all those years of training and character-building asserted themselves and Juliana straightened her back and lifted her head in sudden strength, he relaxed—proudly.

Wilhelmina said, "I am glad to be able to inform you personally that I have just signed my abdication in favor of my daughter, Queen Juliana. I thank you all for the faith you have given me for fifty long years. I thank you all for the affection and warmth with which you have surrounded me all that time. With confidence and faith I look forward to your future under the loving guidance of my dearly beloved child. God be with you and with the Queen. I consider myself happy to be able to shout with all of you, 'Long live our Queen!'"

Then Princess Wilhelmina led the cheers, the traditional three times three. "Hip! Hip! Hurrah!"

To time each cheer Princess Wilhelmina threw her clenched fist upward in vigorous exuberance; each swing of her arm was as strong as the last. So small and sturdy and indefatigable she looked that to all the cheering, weeping people she seemed the spirit of Holland incarnate.

Princess Wilhelmina stepped back and, turning, reached up and kissed her daughter. The Dutch like to say that Juliana's reign began with a kiss. Then Wilhelmina pushed her gently forward. Standing in front of the microphones, Juliana began her reply. Her voice, soft at first, grew stronger as confidence flowed toward her from the people:

"I thank you, dear Mother, for introducing me this way. I feel that it is a great sorrow that in the future we will have to do without your wisdom and experience and, above all, yourself as our Queen. . . . One thing we can do for you is to follow and realize the ideals for which you have always stood so firm.

"Especially I appeal to our youth to endeavor to make a future in which those high ideals for which so many of us gave our lives will be preserved. For myself I appeal to the faith of all of you, the faith you gave me during the five months I acted as my mother's regent.

"Together we shall go forward courageously. Long live our Fatherland!"

As Queen Juliana finished speaking, the crowd, spontaneously and with no signal or sound of drum, began to sing the National Anthem—*Wilhelmus van Nassau*, in which William the Silent, who freed the Netherlands from Spanish tyranny, is supposed himself to be speaking:

> William of Nassau, scion
> Of a Dutch and ancient line,
> I dedicate undying
> Faith to this land of mine.
> A prince I am undaunted,
> Of Orange ever free,
> To the King of Spain I've granted
> A lifelong loyalty.
> A shield and my reliance
> O God, Thou ever wert,
> I'll trust unto thy guidance,
> O leave me not ungirt,
> That I may stay a pious
> Servant of Thine for aye
> And drive the plagues that try us
> And tyranny away.

While the crowd was singing, Princess Wilhelmina tried to slip away. But Juliana gently caught her arm and held her close beside her until the song was done. As it ended, Wilhelmina disappeared into the Palace, and three little princesses came tearing out on the balcony, smiling and waving to the crowd. They changed the whole mood from sadness to youth and joy and hope.

Spontaneously as before, everybody began to sing at the top of their voices *Oranje Boven*—"Orange Above."

At this tremendous moment a telephoto picture of Prince Bernhard showed him with his head turned away. This was interpreted by some people as indifference, which distressed him very much. For the truth was that Bernhard had turned his head away to hide his tears.

HELEN CATHCART

A Traveling Queen

Elizabeth I of England was famous for her tours from castle to castle. They called them "progresses" in those days, great processions on horseback and in carriages, flags flying, trumpets blowing.

Queen Elizabeth II goes on tour today from country to country, covering the world by jet plane, appearing in person or on television.

Today's Queen Elizabeth of England is a queen of the space age. She was twenty-five years old, already married and the mother of two children, on tour in Kenya, when news came that her father had died. She flew swiftly back to London, and was crowned on June 2, 1952, the sixth woman to rule as Queen of England.

ON OCTOBER 4, 1957, Russia launched the first earth satellite, Sputnik I, and inaugurated a strange and unfathomable new era in human history. The news was still being discussed eagerly

From HER MAJESTY THE QUEEN: THE STORY OF ELIZABETH II, by Helen Cathcart.

when Queen Elizabeth II sat nervously before two television cameras set up in the State Dining Room at Buckingham Palace for her first television rehearsals. The two events superficially had nothing in common and yet both were linked in the new modern idiom of endeavor. The space age had begun and the thirty-one-year-old Queen, determined to conquer a new medium, had agreed to broadcast to her Canadian peoples by television from Ottawa on October 13.

It was twenty-five years since her grandfather made the first Christmas radio broadcast and after the animadversions of her 1956 Christmas sound broadcast her Majesty recognized that she must progress to vision. It was indeed a medium her husband had already conquered, first in short talks and then in longer programs. In July the B.B.C. made a film to demonstrate the various techniques available to her: to chat impromptu or frankly read a speech, to read while glancing at the camera occasionally or to look directly at the camera all the time, watching the words of her script flashed before the lens by teleprompter. The Queen studied this instructive film at Balmoral and, guided by Prince Philip's experience, chose the teleprompter method.

It was the responsibility of the B.B.C. team at the Palace to rehearse the Queen and make a telerecording to guide Mr. Michael Hand-Smith, the C.B.C. producer in Canada. The Queen did a run-through and then a "take." Her face was taut, her normally low and pleasant voice strained and high in pitch through nervousness. The producer pointed out these beginner's mistakes and she tried another run-through, but next day the Queen and her husband saw both the telerecordings and found them so disastrous that the Queen decided, on the Duke's suggestion, to scrap them and do the whole thing again.

Meanwhile, her Majesty had to have an inoculation for Asian flu, then rife in America, and to rehearse the script of a speech to the United Nations. Time was needed for her hairdresser and for last-minute wardrobe fittings. The following day, a Thursday, she had just returned from the memorial service to King Haakon of Norway when two more telerecordings were made. On the Friday the results were viewed in the Palace billiard room, and, still short of the desired effect, a telerecording "for guidance only" was flown to Canada.

On the Saturday the royal couple themselves left London airport at 7 A.M., arriving in Ottawa that afternoon. That evening the Queen achieved the extraordinary feat of shaking hands with five hundred people in under an hour at a press reception. Next day she laid a wreath at the cenotaph and attended Divine Service at Christ Church Cathedral. But that afternoon she was still miserable with nervousness as she undertook her television rehearsals and faced the first hurdle of the tour, the broadcast.

The Queen kicked off her shoes as she sat at the desk for the run-through, but the producer noticed the "expression of congealed terror" in her eyes as the broadcast was about to begin. Prince Philip had, however, a card of his own to play. "Tell the Queen to remember the wailing and gnashing of teeth," he directed. The phrase obviously had some special meaning. The mystified director did as he was bid. The Queen flashed a smile of instant amusement and next moment, visibly eased, she was on the air.

"When my husband and I were leaving Canada last time, in the teeth of a gale, as you may remember, we heard kindly people at Portugal Cove singing, 'Will ye no come back again?' Now, after six years, I want you to know how happy I am to be in Canada, once again, particularly at Thanksgiving. . . ."

The broadcast was a long one, in both English and French. "There are long periods when life seems a small dull round, a petty business with no point, and then suddenly we are caught up in some great event . . ." the Queen drew to her conclusion. "I hope that tomorrow will be such an occasion."

This first broadcast was proclaimed a triumph. Relaxed and free, the Queen probably found no ordeal in the great event she had in mind, the opening of the Canadian Parliament, when she wore her Coronation gown and read the speech from the throne under film arc lamps that brought the temperature to ninety-three degrees.

Could it be claimed that royal speeches were phrased in platitudes? The Queen recalled the words of the first Elizabeth to her last Parliament, "*Though God hath raised me high, yet I count the glory of my Crown that I have reigned with your loves. Now . . .*" Queen Elizabeth II continued fervently, "here in the New World, I say to you that it is my wish that in the years before me, I may so reign in Canada and be so remembered. . . ."

There had been some heart-searching to decide whether it would be appropriate for the Queen to land in the United States at Patrick Henry Airport, named for the rebel who wanted liberty from English rule or death. The Queen landed by R.C.A.F. plane and tried to make it very clear in four speeches in the next eight hours that she thought it a wonderful idea to commence her visit at the place where the American nation had been born three and a half centuries before.

"The settlement in Jamestown was the beginning of a series of overseas settlements made throughout the world by British pioneers. Jamestown grew and became the United States. Those other settlements grew and became nations now united in our Great Commonwealth. . . ."

So said the Queen. The Suez crisis had impaired Anglo-American relations, and in the next four days the Queen restored them. She joked happily about George III. She visited the restored Colonial capital of Williamsburg with appreciation and delight, for was not every brick a reminder of the Anglo-American past? In Ottawa, she had slept in the oval, gray-blue royal bedroom of Rideau Hall. In Williamsburg the whole of the one-hundred-room inn had been prepared for her, and the following night she slept in the White House. "My, you look pretty!" said Mamie Eisenhower in welcoming her.

An official program can give no indication of personal impressions. The rather silent onlookers of 1951 were replaced now by crowds who cheered with happy noise, as if television had made the Queen a more familiar and friendly figure. In the 1951 visit an early winter had stripped the trees. Now the autumn foliage was still gilded and glowing.

At a press reception the Queen was asked, "How do you survive your terrific schedule of appearances?" and she had replied, "I survive by enjoying myself every minute of the day." Now she manifestly enjoyed President Eisenhower's huge bubble-topped car, the novelties of arrangement of the banqueting table at the White House, a visit to an art gallery where she saw some of her own Blake watercolors on loan, her visit to a ball game, and her impromptu exploration of a self-help supermarket. (Here the Queen was shown round by an assistant, because the manager had thought the news of her coming was a hoax and had gone home.)

Then an afternoon with Mr. and Mrs. Paul Mellon, kinsfolk of a former U.S. ambassador in London, blended both her best-known and least-known interests, for the Queen visited the Middleburgh race-training track and the Mellons have a notable art collection. Private hardships, too, were moderated, for the British Embassy, for example, notably eased its reception line and the Queen was called upon to shake only twelve hundred hands.

But the most personally memorable day of the tour was doubtless the long-awaited day in New York. Arriving by train from Washington, the Queen sailed across the harbor in an Army ferry so that she might enjoy the famous view of the skyscraper skyline.

"Fabulous! Exciting!" she exclaimed, as so many have exclaimed before her. But for the Queen's special greeting guns thundered in salute, bands played, avenues of fire floats flung their feathery columns of water high into the air, and at the Battery a bubble limousine waited for the ticker tape ride up Broadway. Up to this moment there were perhaps only two major accolades in the world that the Queen had not received—the Broadway welcome and a standing ovation by the United Nations General Assembly—and both were granted on that day of October sunshine.

"Welcome Liz and Phil!" said every shopwindow, but how does one measure a Broadway welcome? Regrettably, the Queen could not share her enjoyment with Prince Philip, for their hosts had prescribed that they should ride in separate cars. The crowds stared yet were not particularly demonstrative and the Queen's view was obscured by falling paper. In announcing that two hundred tons of paper was removed from the street, the City Hall claimed no record.

Arriving for the civic luncheon (with fifteen hundred places) at the Waldorf Astoria, the Queen may not have noticed that she entered by a side door. It was a local joke that the hotel had attempted to lay a red carpet of "fuzz" cement and it had failed to dry, and yet perhaps this epic attempt at a red carpet conveys the welcome best of all.

Then, that afternoon, when the Queen was introduced to the United Nations Assembly, every seat was occupied and people were standing nine deep. The Queen has sometimes complained of "butterflies in the tummy" when opening Parliament. Now her speech was broadcast to the world, filmed and televised, but her composure and calm were notable.

It is so often thought that the Queen's speeches are written by others. Methods vary and have changed with the years, but many speeches are built around the Queen's basic notes and she always says what she wants to say. On this occasion she felt it right to stress the risk that the English and American peoples might take one another for granted. The United Nations was "still far from the achievement of the ideals" of its founders, but the Queen affirmed that the Commonwealth nations could be pledged to add their "tried element of strength and of accumulated experience."

Later that afternoon, from the top of the Empire State Building the Queen looked down on the city. "Well worth it," as she said, when her guide apologized that she had soiled her gloves on a ledge. That evening she dined with four thousand people at a banquet sponsored by the Pilgrims and the English Speaking Union and afterward went on to a Commonwealth ball. It was two o'clock in the morning before her plane left Idlewild.

"Strong men have broken covering this royal runaway race," Bob Considine suummed up. "There isn't a clear eye left, except Elizabeth's."

At Christmas, in 1957, the Queen made her first televised broadcast from Sandringham with few qualms. "It is inevitable that I should seem a rather remote figure to many of you—a successor to the kings and queens of history. . . . But now at least for a few minutes I welcome you to the peace of my own home." That this was possible, she continued, was an example of "the speed at which things are changing. . . . In the old days the monarch led his soldiers into battle. I can do something else. I can give you my heart and my devotion. . . ."

It harmed no one to see the Queen smile with relief at her husband, who was beyond camera range, as the broadcast finished. Oblivious of his mother's skill, it delighted Prince Charles to see himself on a monitor screen before the engineers packed away their gear.

The nine-year-old Prince had now completed his first term at Cheam with a good report and he was bringing young school friends home, a sufficient proof that his parents had not erred in making him the first heir to the throne to go to school.

Princess Anne was similarly not immured with her school books and her governess as the Queen had once been, but had two friends of her own age to share her lessons, and her fun. She was free to a great degree of the adulation that had swamped the Princess Elizabeth in childhood, and could comfortably be taken on explorations of London without being recognized.

On the other hand, on eighty-eight autumn days there had been sixty-eight stories in the newspapers about Prince Charles's life at Cheam, despite the plea that he should be permitted to enjoy his school life like any other boy.

An unhappy rash of royal gossip paragraphs ran through the popular newspapers at that period. Often the gossip, though trivial, was sufficiently accurate to cause concern. In royal homes, as at Cheam School, the staff felt the strain of suspicions that one of them was an informer. What could usefully be done about it? The Queen seldom complains and rarely expresses dissatisfaction, but under the provocation Commander Colville wrote to the General Council of the press, "Her Majesty considers that it is not too much to ask that she and other members of the royal family should receive the same privacy in their homes as is enjoyed by others," and early in 1958 he attended a meeting of the Council to testify to the "increasing disruption" of royal privacy and to ask for guidance on the matter. Subsequently a conference of newspaper editors was called at Buckingham Palace: none could but agree that it was better for Prince Charles to be at school rather than in seclusion under tutors, and the Cheam stories ceased.

The Queen hesitated to claim further privacy for herself, yet she had sufficient cause to remember Bagehot's axiom, "Secrecy is essential to the utility of English royalty. Above all things our royalty is to be reverenced and if you begin to poke about it you cannot reverence it. The charm of royalty will be gone. Its mystery is its life. We must not let in daylight upon magic." Bagehot could rightly say that "Royalty is a government in which the attention of the nation is concentrated on one person doing interesting actions." But television, the microphone, the keyhole camera, the fortunes offered for servants' reminiscences, made fuller privacy all the more essential. The bulk of men and women in royal service had signed an undertaking not to divulge matters concerning their employment. The Queen and her husband had drawn a line of "thus far and no farther." Their public dedication was complete and unconditional but the frontiers of their private life were henceforth to be guarded with sterner vigilance.

These tensions, coupled with a measure of overwork and the exhaustions of travel, may have told on the Queen more than anyone realized. She caught a feverish chill while at Sandringham and in April at Windsor had to go to bed for nearly a week with a heavy cold. It was surprising she did not catch cold in June, when she rode unprotected in the Trooping the Color ceremonial in pouring rain. In July, instead of her customary good health, she was acutely stricken with a painful attack of catarrhal sinusitis and had to spend some days in bed at Buckingham Palace. Probably the Queen was rueful, for 1958 had been planned as a "restful" year.

The "restfulness" nevertheless was relative. The snow flurries of March brought the state visit to the Netherlands, a return for one paid by Queen Juliana and Prince Bernhard in 1950. This was the first time a British ruler had visited Holland, and the Queen elected to sail in *Britannia* from Harwich, the civic occasions of the route thence through Essex enabling more flags to be studded over gaps in the Palace map. But the flags represented towns and the townspeople and the Queen's extraordinarily close attention to detail can be shown by the now celebrated instance of 105-year-old Mrs. Locke, who had received congratulatory birthday telegrams from the Queen, but had never seen any member of the royal family. The royal car was passing through her native village and the Queen agreed to stop long enough for the old lady to be presented.

The local Rector arranged to take Mrs. Locke to the scene of the meeting by car and it was thought that the presentation would occur in the road close to the Queen's car. But then a special message was sent that Mrs. Locke was not to leave her car if it was raining and that the Queen would come over to her. And clearly the Queen then gave further thought to the hazards of excitement to an old lady, for her secretary then wrote to arrange that, wet or fine, Mrs. Locke was to stay seated in her car and that the Queen would speak to her. (The photograph of the smiling Queen speaking to Mrs. Locke through the open door of the car is one that the author personally treasures, for surely this is the quintessence of gracious and kindly royalty?)

Nor was this all, for the Queen heard that the wife of the Mayor of Chelmsford was in hospital recovering from a fractured thigh and grievously disappointed at missing the royal visitors. The Queen thereupon decided to prolong her schedule a little and visit the Mayoress in hospital, not forgetting a gift of roses. The visit, however, was supposedly on the "private" side of the Queen's existence and only the hospital matron and a doctor were present. As a result, the incident was scantily reported, and like many good deeds remains little known.

In Amsterdam similarly the Queen visited the diamond-cutting plant of the Asscher brothers, who had cut and polished the nine pieces of the great fist-sized Cullinan diamond fifty years before, and for the first time her Majesty specially wore the immensely valuable brooch made from two of the larger stones, "Granny's chips," as she calls them. This she took off, asking that it should be shown to the one surviving partner who had been present at the cutting. "I brought them along," she explained, "thinking that he might like to see them again." This true thoughtfulness for an old gentleman—entirely the Queen's own idea—was the story of the week in the Dutch papers.

Yet the program of the Netherlands visit produced many memorable and individual moments: the nautical procession along the eight miles of the North Sea canal to the first glimpse of the turrets and towers of Amsterdam, the visit to the Rijks-museum where the Queen saw Rembrandt's great "Night Watch" and was able to compare the kinship of the Dutch paintings with her own. The Queen renewed her wartime acquaintance with the retired sovereign, Princess Wilhelmina, who had been Queen of the Netherlands when Queen Victoria was on the British throne. There was a visit to the fishing-folk of Scheveningen, a flower auction at Aalsmeer, and much more to give pleasure, to the concluding novelty when hundreds of champagne glasses were raised on the Rotterdam quay to bid Queen Elizabeth farewell.

Later, in this planned "year of leisure," the Queen visited Lincoln, Northumberland, and Scotland, where she caught a severe cold while in residence at Holyrood House and, as we have seen, she was laid up at Buckingham Palace with sinusitis instead of carrying out a planned tour of Wales. This was particularly irksome, for the principality was observing a Festival Year and the Commonwealth Games were being held in Cardiff.

The Queen had agreed to travel through five counties to receive some five hundred people in presentations and to attend the closing ceremonies of the Games. All this had to be abandoned, but there was still something in reserve. The closing scenes were televised and the Queen was watching in London as the Duke of Edinburgh introduced a recorded message from her Majesty to close the meeting.

In the packed stands, and indeed throughout Britain, people watched and listened. "By a cruel stroke of fate," the Queen began, "I have been prevented from visiting North and South Wales today . . . all the activities of the Festival of Wales have made this a memorable year for the Principality.

"I have, therefore, decided to mark it further by an act which will, I hope, give as much pleasure to all Welshmen as it does to me. I intend to create my son Charles, Prince of Wales today. . . ."

The crowds rose in a roar of cheering. The engineers had the presence of mind to stop the sound tape as hats flew in the air and Welshmen danced with excitement. As she sat at Buckingham Palace, the Queen could watch the scene, aware surely of the emotion that swept people everywhere in their homes. Amid the sustained cheering some of her last words were lost. "When he is grown up I will present him to you at Caernarvon."

The Prince had been permitted to watch with some friends in the headmaster's sitting room at Cheam. How right it was that he should be congratulated by his own comrades and contemporaries on receiving in such contemporary style the most important title that it lay in his mother's power to confer.